Robert Llewellyn was born in 1956 and educated in various Midlands schools before becoming a professional hippie craftsman. He graduated through rune-decorated leather work to orthopaedic shoes, living in a variety of squats and furniture lorries until he stepped on to a stage at twenty-five.

He has been writing all his life. His first novel, *The Case of the Brocen Lok*, amounting to a full twenty-five pages, was completed when he was nine. His stage work provided an outlet and he wrote sketches, plays and Channel 4 sitcoms throughout the 1980s, culminating in the prize-winning *Mammon, Robot Born of Woman* in 1988. He has appeared in *Red Dwarf* since 1989. His first book, *The Reconstructed Heart*, was published in 1992 and *The Man in the Rubber Mask* was published by Penguin in 1994.

ROBERT LLEWELLYN

THIN HE WAS AND
FILTHY-HAIRED

I have left Dubai
to start my life ..
Good luck me !!

Jacqui

Feb/6/97.

PENGUIN BOOKS

PENGUIN BOOKS

Published by the Penguin Group
Penguin Books Ltd, 27 Wrights Lane, London w8 5TZ, England
Penguin Books USA Inc., 375 Hudson Street, New York, New York 10014, USA
Penguin Books Australia Ltd, Ringwood, Victoria, Australia
Penguin Books Canada Ltd, 10 Alcorn Avenue, Toronto, Ontario, Canada M4V 3B2
Penguin Books (NZ) Ltd, 182–190 Wairau Road, Auckland 10, New Zealand

Penguin Books Ltd, Registered Offices: Harmondsworth, Middlesex, England

Published in Penguin Books 1996
1 3 5 7 9 10 8 6 4 2

The author and publishers gratefully acknowledge the following
for permission to reproduce copyright material:
The Essex Music Group for an excerpt from 'Won't Get Fooled Again'
by Pete Townshend; © 1971 Fabulous Music Ltd, London sw10 0sz.
International Copyright Secured. All Rights Reserved.
Sony Music Publishing for an excerpt from 'Absolutely Sweet Marie'
by Bob Dylan; © 1966 Dwarf Music/Sony Music Publishing.

Set in 10.5/12.5pt Monotype Bembo
by Datix International Limited, Bungay, Suffolk
Printed in England by Clays Ltd, St Ives plc

CONTENTS

For Mum and Dad

To live outside the law, you must be honest
BOB DYLAN

I

Thin He was and Filthy-haired

'You stupid little prick.' Jeff paced up and down in the gloom of the dark hallway. 'How long have you been doing that?'

'Only the last couple of weeks,' I said defensively, standing in the rear basement room shivering from the cold and the shock of his verbal onslaught. I could smell the dry stench of gas as Jeff walked up and down the damp corridor. I decided I hated him. He could only call me little because I was younger than he; I was sixteen, he was about twenty-eight. I was six foot tall, he was about five foot three. Five foot three of dangerously powerful muscle, in contrast with the six foot of my astonishingly willow-like frame. His thick red hair hung long down his back, longer than mine. His droopy dark moustache sat solidly around his mouth and his deep, northern voice made me feel very alone.

He was standing underneath the problem, a coin-fed pay-as-you-go electricity meter. The box that hung beneath the contraption was designed to collect the coins and it was periodically emptied by a man from the electricity board. The small black enamelled box had long ago been jemmied open and emptied by an itinerant drug abuser. No one knew who did it; it wasn't me, but I was guilty of 'feeding the meter' for two weeks. Feeding the meter, one of a list of previously unknown petty offences which I was picking up on day by day. This particular act consisted of pushing the same ten pence piece into the slot, turning the key and building up time on a small dial. The more I pushed the same ten pence piece through, the more time I could run the lights and fire. There was a reassuring clunk as I turned the key; I watched the needle climb up by twenty minute increments then waited for the coin to rattle into the empty metal cave where the cash box was meant to be. Now I looked into that black cave. It was like my stomach. Big, black and hollow. Empty and pointless. Failed, broken and embarrassing.

'You stupid prick,' said Jeff, dropping the 'little' reference. I didn't gain much succour from this. The word 'prick' sounded small and sharp, like a dog's penis. 'The law'll be round now, man,' he said, rubbing his forehead. 'As if things weren't bad enough without you shagging it all up. I'm on parole, man. You don't know what that means, do you?'

I shook my head slightly. He slapped his forehead and pulled his long hair back with both hands.

'It means I done me bird and I been let out early. If they think I jemmied this thing, or that I've been feeding it, I'm banged up without my feet so much as touching ground. You pillock. Why didn't you tell someone the bloody thing had been broke into? I've got to keep me nose clean. You'll go down for this, you know. I'm not carrying the can for you.'

I looked at Jeff, feeling my brow furrow. I had never thought for a moment that there would be any repercussions from me feeding the meter. I had just recycled that coin again and again, watching the units build up. It meant I could listen to Crosby, Stills and Nash on the big stereo in the back basement room, sit by the electric fire and draw cartoons. I'd felt safe during those periods for the first time since I left home. Now I was going to go to prison for feeding a meter. Jeff had quite clearly stated that I could go down for the offence. Jeff must know, he'd been in prison and had the tattoos to prove it. Done with a biro and a needle. A Celtic knot on his muscular forearm. He knew what happened in life, that much was obvious. He'd been to Morocco, he'd been in prison, he'd even lived in Notting Hill. He was born in Sheffield and he knew stories about the men from the steel works. Stories told in the evening around the pitiful electric fire in the downstairs back room.

'There's, like, a roof-mounted crane in the big smelting works, runs the whole length of the shed. It carries this great, like, like, pot thing they pour the molten steel from. Molten steel, man, that is hot, like ten thousand degrees. Once, this bloke and his son were riding the crane, they weren't meant to, but it were the quickest way to get from one end of shed to t'other. It was a regular thing, lads'd hop on the hook and take a ride in the sky. So this bloke and his son were riding the crane and the son slipped and fell into a massive vat of, like, white-hot molten steel. As his body sank into the burning metal, blood came out of his mouth, his nose, just like, gushed, even his eyes. He were being burnt alive in white-hot metal. He looked up at his dad and screamed for mercy. "Do it Dad!" he screamed, "For God's sake, do it!" His dad reached down and pressed his son's head down wi' 'is shoe, pushed his own son into the molten steel to kill the fucker.'

The night Jeff told me this I was transfixed, seeing every moment of this lurid event in vivid detail. But something worried me, it didn't quite hold together. 'What, so the crane driver saw the son fall, did he?' I asked innocently.

'You what?' snapped Jeff, using the same expression he used when he saw the cracked-open electricity meter.

'You know,' I said, 'when the son fell in the molten metal thing, was the crane still moving along, or did the dad control the crane?'

3

'You what?' said Jeff.

'Well,' I said, ignoring the look of hostility on Jeff's face. I knew he'd calm down once I had explained my problem. 'There's the two men on the crane, right. And it's moving along, like a gantry thing. And up in the top there's a control room where some bloke is controlling the crane. So the son falls off into the metal, but the hook would still be moving. Or did the crane move really slowly so the dad had to push his son down really fast?'

'You what?' said Jeff again, the annoyance now clearly showing in the tightness around his mustachioed mouth. This time I picked up on the fact that he was getting annoyed by my questions. I was creating social embarrassment without knowing how, but I was aware that something was wrong. We weren't alone when I heard the tale, we were sitting in the back basement room with the entire household. We had just eaten a communal meal of overcooked rice, vegetables and chicken. We sat on mattresses covered in Indian bedspreads and hand-knitted patchwork blankets. The plates were on the floor by our feet, some already adorned by stubbed-out cigarettes and joints.

Jeff clearly didn't like my questioning his story, not in front of all these people.

'What you on about, man?' he asked, drawing hard on a thin roll-up. 'What d'you think he did? Dance a jig first, or what?' He looked around the room for support in his belief that I was a pillock. 'Listen, he pushed his own son's head under the molten metal, man, quick, to stop the pain. That was all he could do. That's the point.'

I nodded in apology. I said, 'No, it's just that, well, I suppose I imagined the dad seeing the son burning alive as he was carried away by the crane, you know, if the crane was moving and they weren't meant to ride on it, I

4

imagined the driver didn't know they were on the hook, so there's the driver still with his hand on the control panel and down below on the hook, there's the dad shouting out, "Son, Son!" really loud, and there's the son burning to death in agony going, "Aaaaaargghh!"' I re-enacted the son's dying twitches and motioned the blood pouring from his mouth. This didn't help.

Jeff shook his head in disgust and flicked his roll-up into the empty fireplace. Phil, a full-sized Californian with long blond hair who lived in the attic, burst out laughing.

'Aaaaargh!' he said, blowing out a thick cloud of smoke and mimicking my enactment of the son's death. Everyone else started laughing. Phil had obviously made it okay to laugh.

'You can laugh, but the bloke died, that's all I know,' said Jeff defiantly. Phil passed Jeff a large, wealthy-looking joint. 'Take a pull on that, man!' he said. 'It'll erase your fucking memory.'

Jeff made his hand into a cup shape and reinforced this shape with the other hand, holding the joint between his lower fingers. He brought both hands up and covered his mouth like an airline emergency oxygen mask. Then with much preparation he inhaled huge amounts of smoke from the joint and held it in for what seemed like ages. As he exhaled, he said through a tight, smoke-dried larynx, 'Nice one.' Everyone in the room laughed again. I realized with relief that Jeff had decided against stoving my head in.

Phil, the man offering the wealthy-looking joint, was a dealer. Or so it was alleged. I never actually saw him deal-ing, but then what could you see? There was always a con-stant stream of people coming and going from the house, as there was from all the houses in the square. Phil always had a lot of dope to smoke, he wore expensive-looking clothes, big cowboy boots, a huge belt with a lion's head made of brass which rested just above the tightly packed bulge of his crotch. This gave a pretty clear indication that Phil was rolling in money, sex and dope. His girlfriend, Elaine, was loose breasted and fertile looking. She wore wrap-over tops which she stole from the Laura Ashley shop on Little Clarendon Street. They just covered her, not hiding any shape. I didn't find her attractive, but I could tell she had a lot of sex. I could just tell.

Phil never told stories like Jeff, he just sat quietly on a quilted cushion, a wry smile on his face, his big thighs wrapped in light blue flared trousers. He'd roll huge joints and pass them round generously for as long as anyone else could manage to stay conscious. As he gave me one he'd say something like, 'This will blow your brains out, boy,' or, 'You won't remember your goddamn name after a toke on this shit,' in that cool American way which made such ludicrous macho statements sound almost spiritual.

I had moved into the house with the broken electricity meter from my family home. It might have been a traumatic move for my family, but somehow for me it was very mundane, a thing I had been expecting for a long time.

At sixteen I was ready, I knew I was ready, to go off and be a grown-up. The house I was living in was a squat, an old town house belonging to the university. Number 28 Wellington Square, located in the middle of Oxford. The square had a small walled garden in the centre, sprouting a dozen or so large trees. One whole side of the square was being redeveloped by the university, and the buildings we occupied were due for demolition. They had been left empty for a while and due to the constant housing shortage in Oxford, people broke down the doors, changed the locks and moved in. There were ten or so houses in all, each one containing eight to ten people, so the little squatters' community was quite substantial.

There was one room free in number 28 and I had moved into it. It was December 1972, and I'd been a fully fledged, independent, adult hippie for nearly five weeks. I had long hair, a double mattress with an assortment of old blankets, two hand-made pottery bowls, a fork, over a hundred pens, pencils and crayons stored in a large yellow painted Watney's Party Seven beer can and a small suitcase full of cartoon drawings.

I was even living with a girl. I was sixteen years old and living with a girl, sharing a full-time adult-type bed. Sleeping together every night. That's all we did. Sleep. Allie was an Australian I had met during my last year at school. She was a year older than me. I had been expelled, she hadn't, but she still wanted to drop out and live in a commune with me.

Allie and I had talked in her parents' kitchen months before about communal living and sharing possessions and being free from bourgeois social and sexual constraints. It wasn't long after moving into this big house, which in our pre-home-leaving fantasy lives had constituted a commune, that we realized it very much wasn't.

It was just a house in which a very disparate group of people lived, from charming middle-class students who were saving their rent money to Californian dope dealers, from sixteen-year-old runaways to Northern steel-worker refugees looking for a better life amongst the softy Southerners. This didn't stop me pretending that I was living in a commune. I had never let bare-faced facts make too much of an impact on my dreams. With confidence and gusto I told my parents it was a commune.

'We share all the food and cooking and everything. They're really nice people.' I was talking to my mother

7

from a phone box on Walton Street. 'There's this man from Sheffield, he used to work in the steelworks, and one day his brother fell in a vat of molten steel and he had to watch as his dad had to push him under with his foot. There was even blood coming out of his brother's eyes.'

'That's fascinating, dear,' said my mother. 'Are you keeping warm?'

My mother was right to worry. It was cold and wet outside the phone box. My feet were damp in my collapsing snakeskin platform boots. People walked past in the failing light. The house was cold and damp and I couldn't recycle that damn ten pence piece any more. I would have to wait until all these really nice people from my commune returned from their jobs or study with some money for the meter.

Two days later I answered a loud rap on the front door. The hall was dark as there was no electricity. The man from the electricity board had been to the house, repaired the meter and told someone he would have to inform the police. I didn't have any money, and everyone else was working in nice warm libraries or drinking in warm pubs. I was the only person in the house and I'd been standing in the small back kitchen over the lit gas stove, trying to keep warm. I opened the door to see a large man in a long, wet mac. He showed me an identity card in a torn wallet. He was a policeman.

'We've had a report of an electricity meter being broken into,' he said. My world came to an end. I was going to prison. It was the winter of 1972, I'd been free for five weeks and they'd got me. I'd hardly started my career as a cartoonist and I was going to the slammer.

The police officer followed me down the stairs into the dark basement. I showed him where the electricity meter was. He took a cursory glance and then said, 'Has anyone been feeding it while it was broken?'

'Hardly at all,' I said with a shaky voice. 'I mean, I may have fed it the odd ten pence, but hardly ever.'

'Hardly ever?' he said slowly. 'You know that's an offence, don't you?'

'I didn't when I did it but I do now,' I said, trying to sound honest. I should have sounded very honest because I was telling the truth but I knew policemen assumed everyone lied.

He took my name and address and asked me how old I was. 'Shouldn't you be at school?'

I started to tell him that I'd left school the previous summer with an art O level, and that I wanted to be a cartoonist. I followed him up into the hall. 'Actually, various underground magazines have already published my cartoons, *Carfax Comic* being the main one. That's published in Oxford, but some of the national underground and revolutionary magazines will probably start to use my cartoons, well, more or less definitely, I should think. I'll be starting a regular cartoon strip very soon.'

The policeman walked out of the door and down the steps without saying a word. He didn't arrest me and force me to have a hair cut. As I shut the heavy front door I realized that although I'd got away with feeding the meter I was very lonely. I was even prepared to consider an old, balding plain clothes police officer as company. I went back down to the basement, found the single ten pence I had fed the meter with before Jeff found out, pushed it in the slot, turned the key and the lights flicked on. I had about twenty minutes of power. I turned on the electric fire and sat down to draw some serious cartoons about oppression, the revolution and sexual guilt.

2

We are Everywhere

I have often spoken to people who in their youth read *The Catcher in the Rye*. It has been referred to by famous people in print. People like Bob Dylan read it and walked around New York in 1957 and had sexual yearnings and doomed romantic visions. I have heard stand-up comedians make jokes about it, and I have seen it referred to in novels as realistic character background. It was clearly a very important book to a large group of people.

I've never read it. I don't say that with any pride and one day I will get round to it. I also didn't read *Portnoy's Complaint* when I was sixteen like all red-blooded adolescents are supposed to. I was in the mood to reject any and everything which I considered came from straight society – which included extremely sexually explicit material from Jewish American intellectuals.

Abbie Hoffman, on the other hand, filled those criteria but didn't look like he came from straight society. He had a thick mop of long curly hair and a crazy, bespectacled face. A radical American activist, he wrote a book called *We are Everywhere*.

I read *We are Everywhere* and wandered around the medieval splendour of Oxford having weird sexual yearnings and doomed romantic visions. I read this book and believed every word Abbie Hoffman wrote.

The book was the Yippie manifesto. The Yippie party, not an organization I ever came across outside the pages of his book, was Abbie Hoffman's personal fantasy: young people working together to stop the Vietnam War and change society from the ground up. The book also charted the history of a political trial for conspiracy in which Mr Hoffman was a defendant. The conspiracy was connected with the riots at the Chicago Democratic Convention in 1968.

I didn't understand the intricacies of the political arguments, but the pictures were good. There were hundreds in the book, beautiful black and white pictures of American hippies at work and play. Men with amazing long curly hair, droopy jeans and no shirts. Men with incredible, slim, well-muscled bodies, the like of which I'd never seen in England. Pictures of tall, bare-breasted, well-muscled hippie women working in fields. Pictures of long-haired families living in communes in the Californian desert with names like Drop City. Many of these people were smiling at the camera, holding up clenched fist salutes. 'We are everywhere,' they were saying, with incredible optimism and joy. We will take over this society and change it by having long hair and being rather sexy.

I was transfixed by the book. I spent hours slowly turning its pages and taking in the images. It was a thick, heavy book printed on good quality paper in America and imported to England. It smelt different from English books. It was a hippie product and yet it was good quality. The cover had a picture of a naked four-year-old boy walking along a country lane. His hair was long, thick and curly, like Roger Daltrey's only more natural. This child was so confident, so un-hung up by possessions, sexual guilt, nudity, power and money. That's what the picture said. We are everywhere and we are better than the people with the money, the guns, the clothes and the guilt. We are naked, innocent, but powerful. That's why I loved that book, that's why it held my heart for so long. I wanted to know that I was better than the people who mocked me and said I was a sissy for having long hair and wearing strange clothes. *We are Everywhere* made me feel I was not alone, but part of a huge, worldwide, earth-shattering movement.

I wanted to be one of these people, walking easily and coolly through the world. I wanted my hair to look as tangled and unkempt as theirs, I wanted my jeans to hang off me in that uncaring, droopy but well-fitting way. I wanted a stomach that looked like a washboard and broad, loose-hanging, suntanned shoulders.

I also very keenly wanted to know women who lived in communes, who would pull off their shirts on a hot day and scythe grass with their proud breasts being, well, proud I suppose. I wanted to work next to proud communal breasts glistening in the sun. These weren't like the women in the sad pornography I had fearfully bought, these were real women, intelligent women who were active and powerful and definitely had sex with long-haired men.

It was all in this book: hundreds of people who had already become what I dreamed about. It wasn't simply a fashion thing, having the right style of loon pants. It was a way of life, one that I wanted to discover for myself. Abbie Hoffman was almost alone in helping me. When I eventually stopped looking at the pictures and read the book, his scatter-shot and often contradictory stances about 'youth culture' and the revolution made invigorating reading.

Revolution: a word used now to describe changes in fashion or car design. In 1972 it meant just that, revolution. The struggle towards the overthrow of the status quo, the dissolution of the ruling class. The unstoppable 'we are everywhere' challenge to the straights, as everyone with short hair was called.

The only people I heard actually talk about 'the revolution' were a group of Oxford students I had met when I was still at school. They classified themselves as many different things, but they seemed to congregate around a small publication called *Carfax Comic* which was the mouthpiece of a loose-knit group of radical anarchists. It was named Carfax after the ancient church which stands in the centre of Oxford.

I met these people through my girlfriend Allie, who had encouraged me to join the Schools Action Union a little before I left school. The SAU was a barely existent organization whose handful of activists in London claimed to be struggling to outlaw corporal punishment, uniforms and 'all forms of fascist discipline in schools'. I had hitched up to London with Allie during the summer to one of their meetings. We wandered around Notting Hill looking for the house where it was being held but we never found it. I bought some joss sticks and a leather pouch from a hippie shop on the Portobello Road and we went back home, so I can't claim to have been heavily involved.

'Skools are Prisons' was one of my favourite slogans from this movement. The spelling of skools appealed to me. Who said we should spell schools with a ch? It was crazy, old-fashioned and almost certainly fascist. In my mind at the time the idea that 'Skools are Prisons' made sense because the only institutions which sanctioned corporal punishment were schools. Even a murderer in prison didn't get the cane if he misbehaved, yet I had merely handed in the answers to a chemistry test written in Morse code and I got six strokes on the buttocks. Six strokes of a heavy cane administered by a smiling, Oxford-educated man with thin features and a weeping eye.

Unlike my upper-class friends, I found this a uniquely unsexual experience; it was deeply humiliating. I felt abused. Sitting in the bath at home with dreadful weals across my small, thirteen-year-old buttocks, I tried to forget the pain. But this single incident turned me from a well-behaved middle-class boy doing fairly well at a very academic grammar school into a bad-tempered rebel. If I met that teacher now, he'd be a very old man but I think I would still smack him around a bit. Not now for the marks on my bum, but for the damaging spiral he set my life on.

'Skools are Prisons'. I liked this slogan so much I decided to scrawl it on the front wall of my own 400-year-old school in Witney. I also added it to the cover of my French text book which removed all need of careful detective work on the part of the school authorities.

It was this misdemeanour, plus the fact that I was found in possession of three copies of *The Little Red School Book*, which resulted in my headmaster advising my parents that I should leave the school.

The Little Red School Book was a Danish publication translated into English and aimed at liberating school-children from the totalitarian regime of the school system. It opened with the phrase, 'Teachers are paper tigers,' which I rather liked. Though it looked good, it was in fact far too long and boring to read, except for the sex bit. This gave the most down-to-earth and detailed sex education I ever had during my time at school. It stated clearly that if you were at school you were too young to have sex and there was no big deal and you could wait until you felt ready. If you did have sex it told you how not to get pregnant if you were a girl and how not to get a girl pregnant if you were a boy. This was the official reason why the book was banned. Not because it more or less encouraged children to burn down their schools and machine gun their teachers, but because it talked about sex in an open and straightforward way.

I had received my supply of the books from the *Carfax Comic* people. They also helped me set up an underground magazine for my school which we called *PUSS*. This stood for Pupils Undermining the Skool System. We produced only one issue and I don't think we actually sold any, but it took up a lot of time that could have been wasted studying for exams. Allie wrote some of the text, I did all the illustrations.

The other inspiration for all this activity was the banned schoolkids edition of *Oz* magazine. I had bought it from a market stall in Northampton when I was fourteen. It was my most prized possession, the only issue of *Oz* I ever bought. It contained some of the most erotically stimulating images a young boy could desire, the cover being made up of beautifully drawn pictures of black women masturbating. Nicely. Inside there were articles written by Notting Hill schoolchildren who were shown wearing caps with very long hair. Then there was a wonderfully obscene cartoon strip of Rupert Bear having sexual intercourse with a 'gypsy granny' which ended with Rupert delivering the immortal phrase, 'Ahh, 'tis done.' I'd always found Rupert a bit pervy and this confirmed it.

All these influences culminated in my involvement with the Oxford anarchists, and in the time leading up to my arrival at the Wellington Square squat I would visit them regularly. I would sit on the floor of their bedsit on Richmond Road in Jericho, eat roast chicken and boiled potatoes, smoke dope, listen to Janis Joplin and The Who and talk about revolutionary things. They were revolutionary to me anyway. The anarchists would talk about hitching to Morocco, getting busted in Berlin and having sex in the park in Oxford during the summer.

They were quite deeply involved and well connected with the political struggles of the period. On one of my visits there were two men sitting on the floor of the room drinking tea and smoking. One was reading a revolutionary newspaper called *Workers Press* or *Black Dwarf* or something like that and the other was talking to Hugo, a member of the *Carfax Comic* group. Their names were Jake Prescott and Ian Purdie and they had just escaped long prison sentences after a prolonged trial for conspiracy. Purdie and Prescott had been in the papers for months, named as conspirators in the Angry Brigade letter bomb campaign.

The Angry Brigade had sent letter bombs to the Home Secretary and various judges whom they condemned as fascists and enemies of the people. Prescott and Purdie had supposedly written the addresses on these letters, or walked past the people who had, or something. Anyway, the case failed against them and they were released. But to me they were real political activists, potential martyrs, people who had put their lives on the line for the revolution.

I don't think they noticed me. I certainly never spoke to them. They talked to Hugo for ages while I rolled a joint, possibly talking about co-conspirators or members of the Angry Brigade. If I'd been picked up by Special Branch thugs that night and interrogated I could have blown apart a huge Western European terrorist ring. If I'd listened to what they'd said, and if in fact they hadn't been talking about solicitors and barristers who represented them in court, which is far more likely.

The lives of the Oxford anarchists and Prescott and Purdie seemed highly glamorous to me as a sixteen-year-old schoolboy. The two people in whose room we met slept on double mattresses on the floor, and definitely had sex with each other because they mentioned it completely casually. Hilary 'related' to Janis Joplin. Somebody said to her one night, 'Of course, you relate to Janis, don't you?' and she nodded. Janis was dead by then and so had already become an icon. Hilary wore the same droopy skirts and bangles, and her hair was a messy red mop tied loosely on the top of her head. The man she lived with, Philip, was tall and gangly, with rubbery lips. He related to Mick Jagger.

In my mind's eye, which I have to say was frighteningly vivid, they had sex together like Janis and Mick would have done. In my mind's eye I would often watch them do it. In my mind's eye Hilary would look up from a gentle love-making position and she and Philip would take pity on me and allow me into their bed where I would make love under their gentle, revolutionary tutelage. This was a fantasy which didn't develop into a story I would later tell my mother.

On two occasions I actually stayed overnight at the flat, sleeping in the cold back bedroom, which smelled of musty leather and patchouli oil. I never had sex with any of the Oxford anarchists, but I discovered something in this bedroom which had a profound effect on me. On top of the small purple painted bedside table was a magazine, the cover of which proclaimed *The Best of Tom of Finland*.

Inside were a series of hand-drawn pictures of extraordinarily well-built men having sex with each other. I found the drawings intensely erotic. Cowboys wearing leather chaps and nothing else. Men in bars having intercourse with other men tied over bar stools. Every conceivable homosexual fantasy was displayed in amazing, top-quality toilet-wall detail.

I say toilet wall because that was the only place I had

17

ever come across anything remotely like these drawings before, dirty scratchings on the wall.

Tom of Finland seemed to capture these desires in men and dress them up, almost make them into art. They fired my fantasy life for an intense period but what I found interesting was interspersed amongst the brilliant doodles: black and white photographs of real men, often dressed in a Tom of Finland style. I found these pictures as erotically dulling as I found the drawings stimulating, so much so that the merest glimpse of a photograph of a thick-thighed man would immediately have a deflationary effect on my throbbing member. I could see their faces and I knew they would be like the boys I had been in school with: bullies, bigots, ignorant thugs who would make me depressed if I met them, make me scared if they looked at me. They were too real. Far too real to have a dream about in a stranger's bed.

As all the inhabitants of the Oxford anarchists' flat were students at Oxford University, I was drawn into another life, another world, away from Abbie Hoffman and the free-thinking, loose-limbed, bare-breasted hippies of America. I stumbled into the tight-buttocked, narrow-shouldered, class-conscious unpleasantness of the British political struggle of the early seventies. It seemed to rest like a cloud over the world. It was fashionable to be pes-simistic: there was going to be a terrible hard time before the revolution. A hard rain was going to fall and this lot were watching the weather forecast on a daily basis. Many people would die, there would be food shortages, elec-tricity cuts, cold, hunger, disease. The whole system was about to collapse because capitalism was so corrupt it would cave in on itself like a cancerous corpse. We had to be prepared, we had to be ready to fight since the forces of reaction would do anything to stop us.

It was while sitting in this small room in Oxford that I first heard The Who's 'Won't Get Fooled Again'. There was a verse I've always remembered:

> And the parting on the left is now a parting on the right.
> And the beards have all grown longer overnight.

It seemed to mean we shouldn't trust politicians. Then there was one of those Who drum breaks with Keith Moon doing all that stuff with his arms and face and then, after a Pete Townsend helicopter chord, Roger Daltrey hit the last line:

> Meet the new boss. Same as the old boss.

These lyrics summed up my attitude to politics. I didn't believe that straight politics could solve our problems; we had to approach the mess from a different place. However, I knew then and I know now that there were huge swathes of people around the world, and even around Oxford, living happy and quiet lives in 1972, who had never heard of Abbie Hoffman, the Oxford anarchists, *The Little Red School Book*, *Carfax Comic*, or had any notion of a class-based political struggle leading inexorably to the revolution.

Leaving the parental home and moving into Wellington Square had a very large impact on my political outlook. The brutal bow of HMS *Survival* ploughed me under within days of my arrival. I had posters on the wall from the Windsor Free Festival, Indian wall hangings and a beer can full of pens and pencils. I didn't, however, have any money. I suddenly realized I wasn't getting a grant to study cartoon drawing. I wasn't getting anything. The students I knew were constantly complaining and demonstrating about their shortage of funds, but they had funds that could be short. I didn't have a bean.

When Allie and I moved into Wellington Square she already had a job, cooking and cleaning in a health food shop on King Edward Street off the High. She came home smelling of garlic and fresh bread dough, angry with me because I had been home all day, probably stoned, definitely depressed, constantly masturbating and with nothing to show for it but a half-finished cartoon about sexual guilt lying on the floor.

I eventually went to what was still in those days referred to as the Nash, slang for the National Assistance Board, which even by 1972 was the DHSS. I knew you could go along there, sign on something and they'd give you money. I was that ignorant, I had no idea what it entailed.

'Why aren't you at school?' asked the concerned assistant in the office which had taken me all day to locate.

'I was expelled,' I lied proudly. 'And I left home because my parents are too straight. I live in a commune but I need some bread. I'm a cartoonist.'

The man looked at me in silence. 'You're a cartoonist,' he said eventually.

'Yeah,' I said. 'But I haven't sold any cartoons yet, although various underground magazines are interested. I've had some published in *Carfax Comic*. D'you know it?'

'I can't say I do. Did they pay you for them?' he asked, pen poised over the relevant box on the form.

'Oh no,' I said and watched him drop the pen. '*Carfax Comic* is a revolutionary magazine aimed at tearing down society. They haven't got any money. So I need some money to keep me going until I can sell some cartoons somewhere else.' I smiled at him as he seemed quite sympathetic, for a straight. He sighed again and asked me if I had been looking for a job.

'I don't want a job,' I said indignantly. 'I don't want to live in straight society. I've dropped out. I want to be a revolutionary cartoonist and sign on the Nash.'

'I see,' came the considered reply. The man then quietly disabused me of my fantasy. The idea of the social security system was to give people enough money to live on while they looked for work. I would have to go on job interviews or they couldn't give me any money. This was a horrific blow to my fantasy life. *Job interviews?* That was almost as bad as being drafted into the US Army and going to Vietnam. I'd have to flee to Canada and live in a log cabin.

After hours of waiting, form filling and suspicious glances, I was sent to another office half way up Heddington Hill where I had to wait even longer, sign something else and then go home empty handed and wait for a giro cheque for the amount of £4.98 to drop through the door. I was going to have to sign on every day because I was a minor or something. The reasons were complicated, but it seemed I fell through the net which was supposed to catch poor people because I wasn't poor, I had middle-class parents, and I'd left home and chosen to be poor, which didn't seem to count. Looking at this from the position of someone who genuinely was poor, I can see their point.

I was feeling the advance effects of depression by the time I got back to 28 Wellington Square. I walked up three flights of stairs to our room, opened the door and stood motionless for a few moments as the scene before me started to build into a comprehensive image in my mind. There was Allie, the first woman I had seen naked, the first woman I had said 'I love you' to, the first woman who had sent me a pressed flower on a small card with the words, 'When I kiss you, my soul is on my lips, I leave it on yours' written on it. She was the first woman I'd had a bath with, the first woman over whose breasts I'd cracked a raw egg. The egg may seem a bit obscure but we'd seen someone do it in a film called *Mysteries of the Orgasm*.

There was Allie, my girlfriend, in bed with Jeff. In our bed. Under my blankets. I can only remember a look, no one said anything. It's that special look: getting caught doing it. But then, I'd never done it, I'd never managed. I'd had more opportunity than most sixteen-year-old males would dream of, I'd spent hours with Allie, naked, and I'd never had so much as a slight flickerette of an erection. I had remained resolutely flaccid for six or seven months in her presence. As soon as she was away I was like a butcher's dog, but I couldn't get an erection at the right time.

I left the room and closed the door. I felt a bit dizzy as I looked round the well-swept hallway. I could hear Allie call my name and get out of bed. She was coming to explain and I didn't want to hear. I went into the landing toilet, old, worn but well looked after by someone. I shut the door and stared into the bowl. Something in my body was telling me I needed to be there although I had no idea what. I leaned forward and vomited aggressively.

The following three days were taken up mainly with vomiting and losing the majority of my body weight. This may have been due to the emotional shock of seeing my first girlfriend having sex with another man, or it may have been due to the fact that these houses had been condemned and the leaking waste pipe from the toilet I had vomited into ran above the kitchen ceiling in the basement below. People in another house in the square had been hospitalized and the rumour was they had hepatitis. That sounded good to me so that's what I decided I had.

Allie moved into Jeff's room without much fuss. When she took her Indian bedspreads, joss-stick holders and prints of rural scenery, what had become my room was strangely bare.

Jeff had a bigger room with more posters, Bang & Olufsen stereo and an erection, none of which I could offer. It was a confusing situation. I seemed to have an erection almost all the time except when I was with Allie. I had decided not to get hung up about it as I knew I was one of the 'we are everywhere' people and I would eventually have sex with a topless American commune dweller who scythed grass in the long, hot summer.

I was very sick for three days, not eating anything, feeling cold and miserable and vomiting every few hours. Allie was as sympathetic as a seventeen year old can be with her pathetic ex-boyfriend. She brought me cups of thick soup which I supped and vomited almost immediately. Jeff was quite nice to me. He came into my room with his hand-rolling tobacco and 'put one together for me'. He gave me advice, which was manly stand-up-for-yourself advice, I suppose. The sort which I rejected but in many ways desperately needed. I had had the feeling for quite some time that I was only theoretically male. Jeff was so utterly male, with tattoos and erections, moustaches and a gruff Northern accent, that he never wondered about it.

'You're got to stand up for yourself, Rob, or people won't respect you,' he said calmly. 'You're all right, mate, but people don't know what to make of you.'

As I lay there smoking the throat-blockingly thick tobacco I wondered which people, and what it was they made of me. 'You live in a fantasy world, man. It's tough out there, you've got to live in the real world. Make your way or you get crushed. You know.'

Something about what Jeff said had a ring of truth about it. I started paying attention to him, feeling him lift me out of the ditch I had slipped into, feeling a little better for the first time in days.

To illustrate his point, I suppose, he started telling me stories of hitching in Morocco, of trust between men in the desert, of brotherhood and the need to back each other up.

'You've got to stand by your mates. I've got mates, Rob, blokes I know I can rely on. You seem to be totally alone.'

Before he allowed me to explain that I did have mates, sort of, he started talking about walking along the road to India and getting midnight truck rides with men from Liverpool. I started to lose the point just before he got to the one about the lethal border check in Turkey. Again this story caught in my imagination. I could see the scene vividly.

'There was this bloke driving the magic bus, man, and he'd come up from Kathmandu, across Pakistan, through Afghanistan and he hit Turkey, right, everyone was ripped out of their fucking minds on some lethal Afghan black. The whole bus was right there, you know, on the edge. They got to the Turkish border and the guards dragged everybody off the bus and got, like, a giant can opener, and just ripped the roof off the bus and found, like, kilos and kilos of grade one Paki black, man. The driver had been set up. You know, this is what I'm saying. He didn't watch out for himself, man, he trusted some really fucked-up people. He didn't have any mates to watch out for him. He was going down for life, man, in a Turkish jail. He just went spare. I tell you, if that was me, I'd have cut me own throat then and there. Anything but that, man.'

Jeff left me alone, I presumed, to have more sex with Allie. I lay in bed and imagined being a long-haired dope dealer, rotting in a Turkish jail. It was easy; I was so thin and felt so sick. On one of my many visits to what passed for a bathroom I looked at myself in the half-broken mirror. I was skeletally emaciated. I had a washboard stomach, just like the American men in *We are Everywhere*. I also had washboard ribs. In fact you could have used any part of my anatomy as a very adequate washing aid. I was bleach white with deathly grey bags under my eyes. I thought I looked pretty good. It was the wrecked look so popular with well-nourished, well-educated, middle-class Anglo-Saxons. Less trendy, I imagine, in the poorer areas of the world, but saying to the post-industrial West, 'I reject you, your wealth and everything you stand for, I'm really poor and sick and I look it.' I had also achieved this look without the aid of intravenously injected drugs.

I lay in bed and counted. I'd been away from home for eight weeks, I'd lost my girlfriend to a Sheffield hippie, I was about to die from malnutrition and I still hadn't finished one complete cartoon strip.

I heaved my shaking frame up to the window of my small back room one morning after hearing a strange repetitive sound float up from somewhere below.

I watched, fascinated, as three men, all with very short hair, worked away splitting logs and sawing up large old building timbers in the next-door garden. The short hair was confusing, as they didn't look like straights. They looked different. A woman joined them and she split a few logs too.

I pulled on my now loose-fitting jeans, my collapsing platform boots and a ripped jumper. I had a quick look in the bathroom mirror. I looked like a prince. My long hair was matted and tangled in the most brilliant way, my hands were thin, bony and sensitive looking. I was the colour of ration-book paper, cheap, mass produced and flecked with grey. I wandered down to the back garden, leaned over the wall and introduced myself.

'Hi, I'm Rob. I'm a cartoonist. I live here,' I said without a lot of conviction.

'Hello, Rob the cartoonist,' said one of the men with a big grin. 'Have you got time between drawing cartoons to split some logs?'

'I don't know if I've got the strength. I've had hepatitis,' I said proudly.

This was how I met Roger, Gary and Steve, three men with darned jeans, not patches like everyone else. Darned with brightly coloured thread. Three men with wives, children and very short hair. I clambered over the low red-brick wall from one life into another. It was that simple.

3

Urban Peasants

The kitchen of the next-door house, number 26 Wellington Square, was completely different in décor and cleanliness from the one I had been living in for the previous eight weeks. The three men lived with their partners, Gary with Helen, Roger with Jean, the woman I had seen log splitting, and Steve with Gail. They each had a child, ranging from a few weeks old in the case of Daisy, Gary and Helen's offspring, to three-year-old Emma in the case of Roger and Jean.

They made tea and toast and sat around a big table together. They talked a lot and smoked roll-up cigarettes, not dope.

'D'you all buy food collectively?' I asked, munching on a thick slice of toast and marmalade.

'We buy food in shops,' said Roger.

'Yeah, but you know it's weird,' I continued undeterred. 'When I lived next door I thought that was a commune. I was really, really stupid. Everyone there is, well, a bit selfish. But this is brilliant, this is a real, proper commune.'

'This is a house,' said Roger. He was the one with the big grin. He used it after saying that, holding my eyes. It was a very knowing but inoffensive, non-patronizing grin. It was a grin which said, 'You know I'm right, I know I'm right and it isn't even a problem.' However, I hadn't come this far, lived away from home for eight long weeks just to hear that communes didn't exist. 'Yeah, I know, but you all live communally.'

'We live together,' said Gary, with an attempt at the

same grin. I could tell there was something going on with these people, but I didn't know what it was. For some reason Gary's grin wasn't quite so convincing as Roger's, and Steve's looked like it came from a man who'd had a bit too much to drink. This wouldn't have been the case on this occasion as it was early in the morning and we were all going to collect firewood.

Gary, Roger and Steve collected scrap wood from various demolition sites around Oxford and brought it back on a thing they called a door-mobile. This was a large old front door mounted on four industrial-gauge castors. They sawed up the dirty old timbers, split them and sold the resulting firewood for fifty pence a dustbin load. It was all very well organized, not at all like the chaotic, drug-smoothed squalor of my first commune. After they finished work in the evening they hung their tools up in a small out-house. They even swept the back garden path and stacked the firewood neatly.

'We're urban peasants,' said Gary. 'We live together in a house, and we chop firewood, we look after our children and we eat food. That's about it.'

'What do you do, Rob the cartoonist?' asked Roger, this time with a slight but discernible amount of animosity in his voice.

'I am a cartoonist,' I said, feeling the term slip away from me. 'That's all I've ever wanted to do, ever since I can remember. Although I haven't actually had anything published, yet. I'm looking for a commune to live in. I'd like to build a geodesic dome in the desert.'

'A geodesic dome?'

'Yeah, it's a design of an unsupported dome-shaped building developed by an American designer and philosopher called —'

'Buckminster Fuller,' said Steve without looking up from producing his roll-up cigarette.

'Yeah. Have you heard of him?' I asked excitedly.

'Yeah. Buckminster Fuller.'

'He contributed to a book called *Approaching the Benign Environment*,' I said, feeling the thrill of being able to keep up with these people for once. I had bought this book from a Cambridge bookshop whilst on a trip there with my mother.

Buckminster Fuller had super-optimistic theories on how we'd all thrive in loving communities once we started living in circular, dome-shaped buildings, how we weren't going to pollute ourselves to death as we could pump all our toxic waste materials into deep space, how everything would improve with the use of low-impact, well-designed technology.

'Load of crap, isn't it?' said Roger.

'A complete load of crap,' agreed Steve.

I was hurt by this. I held Buckminster Fuller close to my heart. I felt I had discovered him personally. I had built a geodesic dome along the lines of the one he described when I was still at school. I had persuaded my art teacher, a closet dope-smoking hippie called Mike Wools, to allow me to make it as an art project. I cut the triangles out of old cardboard boxes I gleaned from a refrigerator distributor in Witney. It was about nine foot high in the middle and had many of the magical qualities of a tent: it leaked rain, felt damp and made you glad you lived in a house.

I sat in it and dreamed of building a hundred foot high dome out of large spars of pine. Like the one they built in Drop City, California. I could wear loose-fitting jeans and a tool belt, have a long pony tail and good stomach muscles as I swung from spar to spar, while a topless woman with long blonde hair split logs below and hinted to me that she might like to have sex any minute.

'All those ideas are crap: Buckminster Fuller, geodesic domes, communes, it's all crap,' said Gary. 'We should know. We used to live in a commune.'

'Did you?' I asked, surprised and slightly thrown. I had started to go off my new friends in a serious way, but if they'd lived in a commune, that was different. 'Where was it?'

'It's still there,' said Roger. 'It's a big farmhouse in Wales, in the Black Mountains, it's called Llanbedr.'

'Llanbedr, right. Amazing,' I said.

'It's a real commune, Robert,' said Roger, making much of the commune word. 'We set it up but there are other people living there now. No one has any private possessions, all the money people earn goes into the communal kitty.'

'Really!' I said. This was sounding better and better.

'There's a big organic vegetable garden,' said Gary, 'and they barter goods with the local farmers.'

'You'd love it. It's very beautiful,' said Gail. She was Scottish and had a nice smile. The other women didn't talk but they looked like they knew a lot.

'They have house meetings every week. They share all the tasks like looking after the children,' said Steve making much of the word tasks.

'It's crap,' said Roger.

'Complete crap,' said Gary. 'The whole thing is total crap. Communes are crap and we've got wood to collect.'

I spent the rest of the day with these intriguing men. It seemed that most of the ideas I held dear they deemed as one form of crap or another, and yet I couldn't classify them as straight. They obviously wanted me to think they were one step ahead of all the stupid long-haired woolly idealists that were hanging around North Oxford.

'All these things you're looking for,' said Roger as he

pulled the heavily loaded door-mobile down Walton Street, 'they're just getting in the way. It's just rubbish, all this long hair, geodesic communal living stuff. It's just getting in the way. You need to pare everything down to the minimum. You don't need any of this shit.'

Roger gestured with one hand around the grey, rain-soaked two-storey red-brick street we were walking along. 'All this stuff that people surround themselves with, it's shit. We don't need it. It just weighs you down, drags you down so you feel crushed by it. All you need to do is see that you don't need it, any of it. You'll be happier without it.'

'Yeah, no, I totally agree with you,' I said. 'All possessions weigh you down. Like, property is theft. I really, really agree with that.'

'I'm not talking about possessions, Robert. Material possessions, we all know what they do. No, I'm talking about ideas. Ideas are possessions too. Ideas weigh you down. Clutter up your life. You don't need ideas.'

'But, okay, but I also think,' I said, stumbling to understand what he meant by ideas being possessions, 'I also think all the old notions of power and, and the army and the family are all utterly fucked up. Especially the family. That's why I wanted to live in a commune, to get away from the family.'

'What d'you mean by the family?' said Roger immediately. 'D'you mean *your* family?'

'Well, no, I mean my family are fucked up, but only normally. You know. I think families are probably fascist.'

'It's just a word,' said Roger. 'Family, you've used it as a weight around your neck. You've made the notion of family a problem, and you're living in that problem, and you think you'll find a solution to that problem but all you'll do is create another problem. There's no such thing as the family, Rob the cartoonist. There's just you, and the other people, and we have to get along somehow.'

We spent the afternoon standing in the freezing rain sawing up dirty spars of timber, splitting them with an axe and loading them into a collection of battered dustbins. I mainly did the loading into dustbins part as I couldn't lift the axe in a very convincing way.

Once all the bins were full we loaded them on to the door-mobile and pushed it out of the back garden of the house and on to Little Clarendon Street. We then made a tour around North Oxford, pushing the door-mobile through the rain. We were delivering wood to various large, red-brick houses belonging to well-paid professors, one of whom was Desmond Morris. I saw him in his front room talking on the phone as we passed. His back garden was home to a few goats and rabbits, and when we pushed the bins through the gate he started waving and shouting through the window at us not to let them out.

'He wrote a book called *Body Language*,' said Roger as he pocketed the £1.50 for three bin loads. 'He observes human behaviour and sees that behaviour as a sign that we all have a series of problems. He sees a lot of problems. He's a very worried man. D'you think he's happy, Rob the cartoonist?'

'No, I think he's really hung up about his possessions and his reputation,' I said, adding, 'of course he won't see his reputation as a possession, but that's what it is.' I was trying to please Roger. It was hard to tell if I had succeeded.

'Yeah. His rep-u-tation.' said Roger, making much of the word. We rumbled on to our next drop-off point.

The door-mobile was a very good invention, cheap, utilitarian and amusing to look at. It did, however, have a major drawback. Due to the high level of rainfall in the

British Isles, all roads are built with a fairly sizeable camber to facilitate drainage. This meant that as we pushed along the fully laden door-mobile it was constantly heading towards the gutter. Every now and then it would jar to a shoulder-shattering halt as it hit a drain cover or a pothole in the road. I was utterly exhausted by the time I got back to Wellington Square. My broken-down platform boots were almost too far gone, squelching and slithering about under my feet.

The tired and hungry group of manly workers walked into the warm and brightly lit kitchen at 26 Wellington Square. The picture in front of us was very reassuring at first glance. The three women and their children stood around the kitchen, where a huge meal of vegetables, fish and rice was cooking in a few big pots on the stove. But to add piquancy to the scene, sitting in the middle of the scrubbed wooden table was a very legal-looking document. It was a notice to quit from Oxford University.

4

Endless 'Layla'

At the age of sixteen I could easily sleep fourteen hours at a stretch. I longed for sleep, I longed for bed, warmth, stillness, silence. The little dreams and fantasies I had as I slowly felt my feet thaw out and my body warm up under the mountain of bedding I lay under would beckon me all day.

In the new house I was living in, 45 St Bernards Road, opposite the Victoria Arms pub, just off Walton Street, I had a single mattress on the floor of my messy upstairs room. My bed was a sanctuary for me and I spent as much time in there as I could. I would be warm and comfortable in it, hearing only the endlessly repeated strains of 'Layla' by Eric Clapton on the juke box coming from the pub over the road.

I was sharing the house with the darned-jeans man, Gary, the one who smiled not quite convincingly, his partner Helen and their baby daughter Daisy. We had moved from Wellington Square to the small two-up, two-down condemned red-brick terraced house with all our stuff on the back of the door-mobile. We must have looked like refugees fleeing Poland in the last war: Helen and Daisy, the baby, wrapped up in a colourful shawl, Gary and I pulling the huge pile of belongings along on the rickety contraption. Now I really began to feel like an urban peasant. I could see the look in the eyes of the people who drove past, staring at this ludicrous sight. They were scared of me. I worried them; they thought I was invading. They didn't want me living near their houses. I realized during that short journey that I had already crossed some invisible boundary. I felt like a refugee: I belonged nowhere, I had nowhere to go.

I thought of the years I had spent sitting in the back seat of my father's car, looking out at people walking down streets who looked to me like they were free. People who could go anywhere they chose, do anything they wanted. Glamorous people, like the three men I had seen on the ferry going over to France at the start of a long and painful family holiday. They had long hair, big backpacks, heavy walking boots and rugged, hard-worn clothing. One was smoking a pipe, right there, in public, not worried his mum would catch him. It took my breath away. I was only fifteen, desperate to be different from everyone I had grown up with, desperately driven by some force much stronger than my intellect, my will-power, even my utterly confused sexual drives. This was a desire to be someone else, actually live the life of someone else, a taller, stronger, longer-haired, more rugged some-one else. Someone with a long nose, thick dark hair and deep-set, intense eyes. Someone who just knew how to stand, loose limbed and ready, someone who knew how to travel, to live and, vitally important, knew what it was like to make love to such a degree that he didn't even need to think about it.

All these dreams died so fast, so young. The bitter reality of keeping fed, warm and vaguely happy took over my every waking moment. As soon as we had unloaded the last damp cardboard box full of possessions from the door-mobile I had to walk back to the other side of Oxford in my by now comically decrepit fashion boots in order to sign on and try and get some money.

A place which rapidly destroyed any remnants of my early fantasy life of glamorous, tautly muscled poverty was the social security office on the Marston Ferry Road at the bottom of Headington Hill. Situated a long walk from any bus route, up a quiet side road in what was a poorly converted wartime army depot, the office was in a ramshackle and badly beaten old building which stank of stale tobacco and poverty. Poverty all over the world smells of pepper. It must be some chemical reaction the human body has to poor food, poor clothes and low levels of hygiene. We start to produce pepper. Old English men are the most peppery.

I sat in the stuffy peppery waiting room looking at all the people there. They filled a new category for which I didn't have a name. They weren't really straight: straight people wore new badly cut and ugly clothes from Marks and Spencer, drove new cars and lived in suburbia. These people wore old, threadbare, badly cut clothes from jumble sales, they swore, they smoked all the time, they clearly had no respect for authority, but their anger, when it showed itself, was hopeless. They had no language to express it. I saw a man with a receding teddy-boy quiff in a tatty fake leather jacket shouting at a social security woman behind the Perspex screen. His bad-toothed wife held on to a fat, dribbling child. They smelt of urine-stained underpants drying in front of a two-bar electric fire. They were poor. They didn't have a burning desire to be poor like I did, they had clearly always been poor, knew no other life but were surrounded by wealth on all sides. This man didn't fantasize about building an eighty foot high geodesic dome in the Mojave desert with a long-haired topless farmer. He fantasized about having a new Vauxhall Victor with a clean interior.

He pointed his grubby, stubby finger at the woman behind the partition and shouted that he wasn't having it, and that he would sort the woman out. He shouted that he'd had enough, that he was sick of being fucked around. He looked around the room for support, which was full of people who were clinging on to the very tattered bottom of the badly made safety net of the social security system. This was in 1972, with less than half a million unemployed people. There were loads of jobs, but they were awful, dreadful, soul-destroying jobs, as I was about to discover. But at least they existed. This office was full of people who just couldn't sort it out.

'It's an electronics components factory. They're looking for semi-skilled people to train up to manufacture electronic control systems,' said the man behind the badly scratched plastic screen. I had been called into one of the booths. You'd be called to number seven, and walk along this row of green painted booths looking for a number seven. There wasn't one. Finally you'd see that there was a number seven written on the corner of a piece of lined, foolscap paper which was leaning up against the Perspex screen.

The man behind the screen was wearing a cheap suit and a cheaper shirt. I had held a dislike for suits ever since I went to grammar school. I thought they were ugly. I still do, but cheap suits are really unpleasant. This man not only wore a cheap suit, but he held his pen between his thumb and the back of all his fingers, upright, like you'd hold a drumstick. When he wrote on my form he pressed so hard you could hear the desk creak. I was fascinated to watch him write: the letters were so small that his words looked like a tiny bacterium had been dipped in ink and its progress mapped out on scientific paper.

Watching someone like this always made the front of my head feel tingly and light, a delightful feeling. It always came about watching people's hands do something. I had watched a potter at a wheel in Cornwall when I was

37

twelve. I had stared as a glass-blower in Bournemouth took a rather attractive glass stick and blew the most ugly representation of a deer I have ever seen. But the gentle manipulation of the glass kept my forehead tingling for hours. I assumed this feeling was what people meant when they said they were fascinated. The word 'fascinated' to me feels like a fuzzy, tingly forehead and a desire to keep staring at someone's hands doing something intricate.

I was given a small grey-brown card with the name of the electronics company written on it. I had another long walk to Botley, the wrong side of the Oxford tracks, a road on which, if I walked for a further fourteen miles, would eventually take me to my parents' house.

The electronics factory was a fifties brick-built, small-windowed place down a muddy, dead-end industrial lane. Inside, another man in a cheap suit asked me to come into a brightly lit room. He offered me a chair and asked me my name and how old I was. I told him.

'Shouldn't you be at school?' he asked.

'I was expelled,' I lied proudly. 'For political reasons, actually.'

'Right, and now you want to work for P & D electronics components?' he said cheerfully.

'Not really,' I said. 'But I have to go for job interviews or the social security people won't give me any money.'

'I see. Well, are you interested in electronics, Robert? Did you study science subjects at school?'

'No, in the end I only did art. I went on strike and wouldn't do any of the other lessons. All the teachers were fascists, and the headmaster thought we fought on the wrong side in World War Two. He had pictures of battleships all over his office walls.'

'So you haven't got any qualifications?'

'Art O level.'

'An O level,' he said, surprised.

'Yeah. In art. I did a painting of Jesus driving to Calvary carrying a stainless steel cross on a fork-lift truck.'

'Did you?' he asked, staring at me as if I were an alien.

'Well, I say painting; it was a sketch using a Rotring pen, a German draughtsman's pen. They're very good. I've got four, different sizes. I coloured the picture using various inks.'

'Right. Well, you're far too intelligent to work here,' he said suddenly.

'Am I?' I said. 'I failed maths CSE and that's supposed to be impossible.'

'Yes, well, I think you'd find the work very repetitive and dull. I don't think you'd be happy here.'

I was shown out, and as I walked back up the muddy track to the Botley Road I realized that this is what most people did with their lives. They didn't just have a choice about going to university or not, they didn't have any choice at all. They just got any job they could and they worked. All this meant was they got paid, which meant they could eat and pay for somewhere to live, which meant they could breed, raise a family and die. It all seemed very bleak and futile and ideally suited to the dull December afternoon I was walking through. I had never been taught anything of use in the last five years of my schooling. I had never had even the most rudimentary aspects of the social security system explained to me. I had no understanding of the National Insurance system or my position as regards the Inland Revenue. All these complex responsibilities were dumped on me suddenly because I had left home and was trying to survive as an individual away from the official family nest. I didn't fit into any category post-war governments had devised, I wasn't breaking the law, well, not any law anyone could think of, but it was clear from the looks on all the adults in authority I came into contact with that I shouldn't really have been there.

I settled into my life as an urban peasant with Gary and Helen. Gary wanted to keep the place clean and tidy and was prepared to go to extreme lengths to achieve this. The interior of our house was very utilitarian: no carpets or soft furnishings, no Indian wall-hangings or big cushions, no joss sticks or stereo system. Everything we owned was hung up from shiny new six-inch nails driven forcefully into the wall with a seven-pound lump hammer. Gary didn't like things to wobble. There was no hot water system so I helped Gary nail a very large plank of wood across the old bath which was in the small lean-to kitchen at the back of the tiny house. On top of this we placed two piles of bricks which in turn supported a twenty-five-gallon cooking-oil drum we'd picked up off the street outside the Neptune fish and chip shop on Walton Street. This had been cleaned out in true urban peasant fashion: it took hours and we used a whole expensive bottle of washing-up detergent to get the thick oil out. We filled it with water and then placed a pressurized paraffin cooker underneath, lit it and sat back on the hard chairs and smoked roll-ups as the water slowly heated.

'Total cost of our water-heating system, thirty-five pence,' said Gary to Helen as she returned with Daisy from one of the other houses up the road.

'Plus all the washing-up liquid,' I said.

'Yeah, okay, but it's still very cheap,' Gary replied defensively.

'Very good,' said Helen, admiring our handiwork. 'You're sure it won't fall over?'

'Of course it won't fall over, woman!' said Gary. He

often called Helen 'woman'. I found it shocking the first few times, but as I got to know Gary I realized he was the least woman-hating of the group I had met in Wellington Square. Clearly the word 'woman' wouldn't appear in most people's list of offensive terms, but it depends how it's said and by whom.

'I nailed it in with some six-inchers, it weighs about half a ton, you'd need an earthquake to shift that.'

'We get earthquakes here sometimes,' said Helen, jigging baby Daisy up and down and smiling to herself.

'Please, Helen,' Gary pleaded, gesturing around the small, Spartan room. 'I'm trying to make a decent home here, you know. It's not easy.'

'It's not easy for any of us,' said Helen, now patting the gurgling Daisy on the back.

'I know,' said Gary, already showing in his tone of voice that he was on to a loser.

'It's hard for all of us. It's even hard for Robert,' she said smiling at me.

'I know,' said Gary bitterly.

'It's not that hard for me, actually. I mean, you know, I don't have a baby or anything,' I said, trying to support Gary a little.

'You see, he doesn't complain,' said Helen.

'All right,' said Gary. 'I don't know what I'm supposed to do. Nothing satisfies you, does it? Nothing I do is any good.'

'I didn't say that,' said Helen. She was still smiling, mainly at me, but clearly for his annoyance.

'I'm going to have a bath,' said Gary, stubbing his roll-up cigarette out forcefully into the housebrick ashtray which stood on the skip-found, wire-and-firewood table.

'Careful,' said Helen, barely stifling a laugh. Gary

looked at me and shook his head in a resigned 'there's nothing you can say to a bloody woman' style.

Gary was clearly happier the moment he was tinkering with his improvised water-heating system. I made a cup of tea for myself and Helen. Gary didn't want one with a vengeance I have rarely seen connected with mere tea. He made much of his descent into the bath. Helen and I discussed the unfairness of child-rearing as Gary could be heard noisily abluting himself in the tiny kitchen.

'It's fantastic,' he shouted. 'The water is really hot.'

'That's good, darling,' Helen responded flatly, still smiling away. What was it this woman knew that allowed her to smile through everything?

Suddenly there was a low thud and a shriek of pain from the kitchen. We jumped and threw back the door. The room was fogged in a dense cloud of steam. Struggling clanging noises and swearing were coming from the bath. Gary was trapped under a scalding twenty-five-gallon drum of water.

'The bloody tap was stuck, the bloody thing fell over,' said Gary as I burned my hands lifting up the drum and freeing him.

'It fell on my fucking head,' said Gary through gritted teeth, sitting naked in the bath, looking thin and vulnerable.

Helen was very supportive and unsarcastic as she mopped up the water on the floor and held baby Daisy. I gave Gary a towel and he started to redesign the water system as he dried himself.

I liked Gary. He listened to my rantings and laughed at my anecdotes. He was a combination of dad and elder brother to me. However, I could talk to Helen so much more easily.

I found it hard to talk to the knowing men, the urban

peasants I had met in Wellington Square. They seemed to use their experience as a weapon, their knowledge as a fortress. I couldn't quite understand why. I didn't see how they could view me as a threat. I was still basically a kid.

Half the square had moved to a row of semi-derelict houses on St Bernards Road, and the urban peasant families occupied three. We all spent a lot of time together over the endless nights of my first winter away from home. The men displayed a bitterness in their approach to life which, like the dark clouds, never seemed to lift. It was a solid, self-assured bitterness. They looked on other people's happiness with a wry smile. They knew, and of course in many ways they were right, that this happiness was doomed to a short life. My joyous enthusiasm for geodesic domes and communes was soon crushed by their all-knowing self-awareness. They liked to drink, but they didn't seem to get drunk. They would come back from the pub over the road and make cheese on toast under improvised grills. They would drink tea and sit on hard chairs in Spartan rooms with a single, bright light bulb and no shade. The women would have gone to bed to get up with the babies in the morning. During these long nights Roger would hold forth.

'What d'you believe in, Rob the cartoonist?' he would ask, staring at me with bigger than necessary eyes.

'Loads of things,' I said, 'but certainly a violent, total cultural revolution, the complete removal of political power from the élite and the establishment of a series of communes which live off the land.'

'Fucking hell,' said Steve. 'He's serious.'

'That's a lot of beliefs,' said Roger. 'Don't you find they tie you down? Aren't they a heavy weight to carry with you?'

43

'Not really. I just think that the system is really screwed up, and it's going to collapse anyway.'

'Have you ever heard of someone called Krisnamurti?' asked Roger, sitting quietly, as though the question was dangerous.

'Isn't he that fat Indian kid that loads of people are into?' I asked.

'No, that's Guru Maharaji Mahesh Yogi,' said Roger. 'Krisnamurti is the exact opposite of him. He's an Indian man who was brought up to be a guru, like Guru Maharaji, but he knew it was rubbish, a con, that there was nothing to believe in, that all belief is baggage that you don't need and that stops you growing.'

'Wow,' I said. 'Brilliant.' This Krisnamurti guy sounded like my sort of fellow. I found the idea of following anyone, even an ethnic person with a smiling face, a stupid thing to do. I somehow knew that they would be wrong and my commitment to them would become an embarrassment very quickly. However, being into Krisnamurti sounded just great, because he said you shouldn't be into him, that there was nothing to be into.

'So you're not Krisnamurti followers?' I said hesitantly.

'No,' said Steve.

'There's nothing to follow. No one to follow. There is nothing.'

'Wow,' I said. 'That's well, it's sort of frightening.'

'Yes,' said Roger. 'It can be very frightening. But then you realize that fear is just another possession, you don't need it and once you let it go, there is no more fear.'

'Wow,' I said. 'So how d'you know about this Krisnamurti guy? Because surely, if he says you can't believe in him, then you shouldn't really know about him, you know, because he shouldn't say anything in case people start to believe in him and screw the whole thing up.'

'Listen to yourself, Rob,' said Roger. 'The noise in your head. You don't need all that.'

He was right. There was an enormous amount of noise in my head: voices, sounds, pictures, questions, colours, shapes, feelings, fears, dreads, hopes and small golden floating things in the distance. How could I silence all this activity, and did I really want to? Krisnamurti would probably say that it was all rubbish and I should let it go. I found this half attractive and half stupid. Surely this noise was what kept me alive, made me a human being as opposed to a cow chewing cud peacefully in a meadow.

Still, Krisnamurti was the best I ever came across, and my admiration for the urban peasant men grew somewhat. They seemed solid and careful, kind in a stern way, presumably loving with their partners, who all struck me as very intelligent women.

I wanted to be like them. I even considered cutting all my hair off. I wanted to have darned jeans, not patched ones, I wanted to wear small leather jackets with no decorations, not my absurd colourful one with embroidered Celtic knots on the back.

Then one night I was baby-sitting Daisy and something seemed to change. All three of the urban peasants came back to our house, not a common event. They sat down and teased me about making them tea and cheese on toast. The teasing was about me being a good little wifely figure, which really didn't bother me. I made them all tea and big thick slices of dripping cheese on toast.

Roger sipped his and then said, almost as if he'd been rehearsing it in the pub, 'You look like you've never tasted pussy.'

I was amazed. I couldn't believe my ears. This was not what I had come to expect from these men. 'And believe me, Rob the cartoonist, the longer you don't taste it, the better off you are.'

'Well, I have as a matter of fact,' I said, almost lying. I wasn't sure if I was lying or not because I wasn't sure what he was on about. Did he mean, actually taste pussy, as in a woman's genitals, as in cunnilingus, basically the only sexual practice I was any good at? Or did he mean the entire gamut of sexual relations between men and women, which I had a suspicion the term pussy was meant to represent, at which I was almost completely ignorant?

'No, you haven't. Not really,' said Roger.

'You're too happy,' said Steve glumly. 'Once you've tasted pussy, you're finished. Once they've got hold of you, they'll never let you go.'

'Who?' I asked, half knowing what he meant but not wanting to believe it.

'Bloody women,' said Gary loudly.

'Yeah, bloody women,' said Roger. 'You're a pretty boy; they like you.' Roger smiled and showed his long row of strong white teeth. 'And before you know it, Rob, one of them will have you, and she'll never let you go. Once you've had a taste of that pussy, that'll be it. It eats away at your brain.'

'Pussy eats your brain. Really does your head in,' chipped in Gary, looking up at me over his glasses.

'But you all seem happy,' I said, completely sober and missing, presumably, a lot of the nuances of what was going on. 'You all live with women, you've got kids.'

'That's just it, Rob,' said Roger. 'That's how they get you. They get you in with their pussy, then they keep you in with the kids. Once you've tasted that pussy, you're finished.'

Roger took a big, man's mouthful of cheese on toast and chewed very slowly. There was silence except for

Steve's teaspoon stirring round and round in his large mug.

'Roger's got three kids,' said Gary, watching me to see my reaction.

'Have you?' I asked, quite startled at the news. I'd only ever seen him with his three-year-old daughter.

'You know Jean, blonde hair, always in the pub,' said Roger, ignoring my response. 'She lives over the back there. Her four year old, Mark, that's my boy. And there's a woman called Sylvie, she lives in Llanbedr, the commune.' He made much of the commune word as usual. 'She's got my other daughter.'

'Wow,' I said. 'How come you've got three?'

'Why d'you think, Rob? Because of the pussy. I can't resist the pussy.'

By now the word pussy was making me feel positively nauseous. I was still technically a virgin, but I knew what they were talking about. What didn't make sense was that they spoke as if they hated women's bodies with a vengeance, and yet couldn't resist them when confronted with the real thing. I spent my night-time hours imagining myself melting between Allie's legs as finally we got back together and she let me have sex with her. I didn't hate her, I didn't want to think that she would trap me with her pussy. I didn't even like using the word pussy in my head, alone, at night.

Apart from the feeling that being trapped into having sex with a woman was in my 'chance would be a fine thing' category, I thought being so frightened of women, which is clearly what these three, big, strong, grown-up men with no beliefs were, was strange and confusing. I had only ever been frightened of other men, and with good reason. Other men were violent and dangerous to sit too close to. At the age of sixteen I definitely thought of men as *them*. Some other strange and alien race of beings with whom I had little or no connection.

I didn't think I was a woman, I didn't want to be a woman, but I clearly did not see myself as a man. And neither, looking back, did many other people. Women often took me into their confidence in a way I now see they rarely do with a man. I spent many hours sitting with Helen, Jean and Gail in various St Bernards Road kitchens talking about children, travelling adventures, old boyfriends and sex.

I enjoyed it, and the unpleasant night of the pussy conversation drove me more away from the men and more towards the women. With them I was hearing something different. Something other than the brutal way of looking at things which all the teachers and schoolboys I'd been brought up with had tried their damnedest to drive into me.

I'd try and join in with the women, holding babies, sipping tea and rolling cigarettes, but something someone said would set me off. I couldn't flow with the conversation. I'd start off a sentence about an idea and it would tumble out as though I were on top of the Malvern Hills: my mouth would start running like mad down the steep incline of my concept. I'd soon lose my footing, flying down and stumbling into embarrassment.

'You see, Roger is really brainy, but he's all twisted up about women and sex. It's really, really common. I know loads and loads of men who are like that, and it's terrible because they're all really unhappy but they sort of push all their feelings out, like being drunk and swearing a lot and, and then they slag off women and think that other men will agree with them and they do and it all gets worse . . .'

'Roger's a good man, Rob,' interrupted Jean after sitting patiently through my badly botched analysis. I was surprised. She had just been very critical of him a few minutes before. 'He's a very special man.'

'No, I know he is. I know he really sees things differently and worries about things,' I said trying to climb back up the Malvern Hills.

'He comes from a very unusual family, you see. He listens to you and he knows, Rob, he's done all the things you talk about before. He built a dome out of wine bottles.'

'You're kidding,' I said.

'No, he really did: wine bottles and concrete. Didn't he, Helen?' Helen nodded, smiling slightly as she always did.

'He formed the commune in Llanbedr,' said Jean. 'He and Gary and Steve used to be in a band.'

'A band!' I said, more amazed with every word. I couldn't picture the strictly behaving urban peasants as a band.

'They all had really long hair, you see. It's difficult for them to be nice to you. I suppose they think because they made a mess of all the things they tried, you will as well. In a way they're trying to be nice, they're trying to stop you being miserable and making the same mistakes.'

'A lot of what they say is right. A lot of hippie stuff is really stupid,' I said. 'But there's some things, you know, that are really important. Like trying to be, well, more humane, and not damage the world, you know, all the more gentle stuff. I think that's important.'

'It is, Rob,' said Helen. 'Don't you listen to them. They're just miserable old men. They're jealous because you're so pretty and young and all the women in the pub fancy you.'

'Do they?' I said, delighted.

'Not all of them,' said Gail drily. Of course Gail was the quiet thin one who had absorbed a fair portion of my

49

fantasy time. As was always the case with me, I only fancied women who thought I was too thin, probably gay, too young, too stupid or too much like a girl.

As the days passed, I saw less and less of the urban peasant males. I didn't seek them out, didn't spend time in the pub with them and started to doubt their ideas, their short hair and their darned jeans. I know Krisnamurti would probably say that doubt was just a way of trying to escape the huge void that is our inner life, that doubt was just clutter, a safety net, but the doubt wasn't something I wanted. I was looking for some men who would show me what to be like. I had never found any. I had read books about Che Guevara: he looked cool in his beret, then I discovered he was a macho bully boy who was handy with a gun. I had read *Playpower* by Richard Neville, the Australian who ran *Oz* magazine, which I found a very depressing experience. I had met Jeff, the thick-armed Northerner who had gone off with Allie. I didn't want to be like him.

The urban peasants were the nearest thing I had come to finding a role model. But they were scared of 'pussy', of women, and that fear was a very ugly one. I didn't like it, and I couldn't follow them any longer.

5

Dark They were and Golden-eyed

Jenny was a regular in the pub opposite the house. She was petite and shared a tiny house like ours with a couple who made their own cheese by hanging bags full of rotting milk solids in their back doorway. Not something you want to walk into on a dark night, which I did regularly.

Jenny and I stood beside a bus shelter in Brecon trying to hitch our way to Llanbedr, the commune. It was New Year's Eve 1972, and there wasn't much traffic. It was cold, and my once stylish snakeskin boots, decrepit for months, were now way past the fashionably broken-down stage. They were in terminal decline. One heel was loose, they gaped open at the sides, they were agony to wear, but I didn't have anything else.

I had blown out a Christmas job that the man in the cheap suit had got me at the Oxford Royal Mail sorting office. I spent three nights throwing parcels into sacks for all the towns and villages around Oxford, where I was brought up and had been to school. I knew if it said Ducklington on the parcel, it went to Witney. The student I was working with, friendly, but rather dense, was from Kent.

'I'm from Kent, actually. I don't know where any of these parcels are supposed to go,' he said happily on the first night. As soon as he opened his mouth I could tell he'd gone to public school. I wasn't sure why he had got this dreadful job, though, since he sounded rich.

'Give it here,' I said and threw it in the correct sack.

After two night shifts where I had sorted all the parcels while he stood holding the odd one while telling me how ugly all the girls were at Lady Margaret Hall, and how African women would suck you off for twenty pence in Rhodesia, he gave me some information which helped me leave. He got paid fifty pence an hour, I got twenty-five. I walked into a painted brick office where a man in a postman's uniform sat behind a desk.

'I only get twenty-five pence an hour, the bloke I work with gets fifty.'

'Sorry?' he said, tired and worn from years of petty problems.

'I know where all the parcels go, he doesn't. He comes from Kent. He gets fifty pence an hour. I only get twenty-five.'

'You're only sixteen,' he said flatly.

'What does that mean?' I asked indignantly.

'Well, you should be at school, shouldn't you?'

I walked out without saying another word. I never got paid a penny. My dreams of saving up my twenty-five pence an hour wages and buying some new boots had stayed in those wretched midnight mail sacks.

Somehow Jenny and I managed to get lifts all the way from the Woodstock Road in Oxford to the entrance of a large, broken-down farmhouse outside Llanbedr. This was the commune that Roger the urban peasant had set up, this is where the urban peasants had lived during all those years of hardship — when they were rural peasants I suppose. This was the house the members paid £4 a week in total to live in. The owner was a farmer who'd built an ugly but warm bungalow up the track, with central heating, telly, garage. All the things the commune dwellers would do anything to avoid.

We walked past the bungalow down a muddy, badly

rutted track, past broken-down farm machinery and gutted cars. A light glimmered in the distance, and Jenny kept encouraging me forward. I trusted her, although I couldn't see my hand in front of my face.

I finally walked in through a low, unpainted wooden door and into a kitchen. I decided then and there I had entered heaven. A huge, chaotic, filthy tumbledown dump. Broken furniture, dogs and children playing on the floor, a vast wooden tub in the kitchen full of steaming hot water. A naked man was standing in it soaping himself. The water was entering the tub from the waste pipe of a broken-down top-loading washing machine which was chewing its way through a clod of grey clothing. The water in the tub was an unspeakable grey–brown colour. Everywhere people were cooking, shouting, getting dressed up, screaming, crying.

Actually Jenny was the only one crying: it was during the first few moments of my arrival that I found out Jenny was pregnant by the man in the tub, and he didn't want her to have the baby. As soon as he'd climbed out of the filthy water and dried off his lean body with a filthy-looking towel, he and Jenny went upstairs to scream and fight. Little acknowledgement was made of this by the rest of the household, who kept appearing from doorways and back passages. I was introduced to so many people I stood spinning, a grin all over my face.

'This is Rob, lives with Roger and Gary in Oxford, he's a cartoonist,' was how I was introduced.

'This is Dave.'

'Hi.'

'Jack.'

'Yeah, all right, man.'

'Juliet.'

'Oh, hello.'

'This is Napoleon,' someone said when a vicar walked into the room. Napoleon the vicar started to roll a joint, he laughed richly and said 'fuck' a lot.

A beautiful Frenchwoman offered me a cup of tea in a filthy mug. Her child clung to her hip, the child Roger had told me about. The woman was Sylvie; I was almost in love. I sat down next to the fire, a huge inglenook fireplace in which were burning several corpse-sized logs. Young men sat nearest the fire, looking at it and poking it with sticks. Dogs lay all around them, lazily absorbing the warmth.

'Party tonight,' said a long-haired person sitting next to me. The person had on so much face paint I couldn't tell which gender it was. 'Builth Wells. Lots of really tshhh people.'

It was a he: I could tell by the size of his filthy hands. When he said 'tshhh' he made the spot-on symbol, a circle of thumb and forefinger, holding it up in the air for slightly too long. He was very stoned. 'Napoleon's taking the Land Rover. You coming for the party?'

'We've only just got here,' I said. 'We hitched from Oxford. I came up with Jenny.'

'Yeah, Chris's old lady,' said the man. I'd never heard anyone use the term 'old lady' before. I'd read it in Abbie Hoffman's *We are Everywhere* book, but I'd never heard anyone say it out loud. 'That's a heavy trip she's laying on him. The baby and everything. That's why I don't get involved in the whole man–woman thing.'

I nodded, wondering what it took in someone's past for them to get this dirty and weird looking. I never realized, before I met this man, that I had a cut-off point for what was *too* dirty. I always wanted my clothes to look well worn, but I spent hours in the launderette on the corner of Clarendon Street and Walton Street watching my jeans

54

grind around in the machine. I liked the feel of clean clothes. This man's clothes were so filthy they were black with grime.

'The party is going to be tshhh. Really,' he said, using the same symbol, gilding it with a gap-toothed smile. I sipped my tea as the large heavy kitchen door smashed open. A pig grunted, louder than I'd imagined a pig could grunt. The door crashed open again and a very large, very dark pig shuffled into the room, running its thick wet nose over the dark brown carpet. It shuffled about, occasionally stopping to sniff something really hard, then moved slowly on. I was stupendously impressed. A pig in a house. Brilliant.

The Frenchwoman came running down the stairs moments later and flew into the room wearing only a bra and long skirt. Her hair was wrapped up in a brightly coloured and possibly clean towel.

'Who let Chipper in? *Merde!*' she said, shooing the disgruntled porker back out.

'The pig just goes where it wants, like us,' said the man with the painted face. We heard the even larger outside door slam, and the Frenchwoman re-entered the room.

'It ees a peeg!' she shouted. 'It is a blady peeg! Little children run round in 'ere. *Merde!*' She rushed off upstairs again. The large ceiling was bouncing up and down as people ran about screaming and shouting at each other. I couldn't understand who lived in the house, who was visiting, who could eat food, who kept the pig out. None of it made any sense at all.

'It's too controlled here,' said Painted Face.

'You don't live here then?' I asked.

'I live in a teepee,' he said proudly. His dog wagged her tail in agreement.

I was amazed. This filthy, long-haired nutter lived in a

55

teepee. Nowadays everybody has heard of people who live in teepees, there have been documentaries about them, people have watched them being torn down by police at Stonehenge, but in 1972, let me assure you, it was unheard of. I couldn't picture it.

'A teepee?' I said.

'Traditional home of the Red Indian.' He shrugged, using the pre-politically correct term for Native American. 'Circular, natural. I couldn't live in a square, stone house. I'd feel all blocked in.'

'Yes, of course, that is why I want to build a dome,' I said, hoping that under the paint there was some sanity lurking. 'A circular home is more natural; Buckminster Fuller said that.'

'Domes are too, I don't know, science fiction. They're not natural. Not ethnic.'

This was the first time I'd heard the word ethnic, though it was to become very popular in fringe circles during the seventies. It didn't refer to people of different ethnic origin from our own, but to old, worn-out multi-coloured bits of cloth made into a shirt from Afghanistan, pointy-toed leather shoes with holes in, strange wrap-around sarong-type trousers, cloth with mirrors sewn into it. Anything that came from anywhere which wasn't influenced by the West, which was made by hand and didn't contain plastic was potentially ethnic.

Another door burst open and Napoleon the vicar marched in, singing loudly about going to a party. Children shouted, dogs barked, more people arrived in long cloaks, strange hats, too much make up. The man who had been in the tub of water when I arrived appeared from the throng. His thick mop of curly hair seemed to stand unrealistically high above his face. He was wearing green tights, size fifteen black wellington boots and a coat that looked like it was made of autumn leaves. On closer inspection it was made of coloured felt. He was dressed as the wild man of the woods.

'Hi, Rob. I'm Chris, we're all going to a New Year's Eve party in Builth Wells. Jenny's coming, but you can stay here if you like. There will be people here with the younger kids.'

'I may as well come, if that's all right,' I said, flashing momentarily on the possibility of meeting a hippie princess with her own farm in the hills. A woman who was prepared to split logs and make love and smell wonderful just like the women in *We are Everywhere*.

'Room in the back of my Land Rover,' shouted Napoleon. 'Got no petrol so it should be an interesting trip.'

I pulled my leather jacket on and followed a group of jangling, shouting people and dogs outside. Napoleon's Land Rover was canvas-topped and quite small, so apart from being humorously cramped, we were assaulted on all sides by skin-burning blasts of icy night air.

As we bounced down a narrow lane towards some distant lights the engine suddenly spluttered, and finally died.

'That's it, no more petrol,' Napoleon said and took the car out of gear. We whooshed through the night in silence. I noticed that the party-goers did look a little subdued. No one was singing, and even the dogs seemed to eye the darkness warily.

'Anyone got any money?' Napoleon asked. I had about three pounds in my back pocket, but that had to last me another ten days. Clearly all of the commune members were running through similar thoughts as a renewed silence fell over the tightly packed group.

'There's only one thing for it then,' said Napoleon, taking a sudden turn to the left. 'Hang on tight, here we go.'

In the darkness it seemed like the road just fell off the end of a mountain. It fell away so steeply in front of us that the car's lights momentarily shone into nothingness. We all started to scream in unison as the vehicle built up what seemed like a cartoon-like speed, somehow accentuated by the lack of reassuring engine noise. Just the wheels spinning beneath us, whining higher and higher, their tread giving us some flighty grasp on the earth as we sped to our doom.

'I've got to kill the lights now or we'll have a flat battery as well,' shouted Napoleon over the roar of the wind. A woman behind me screamed and grabbed my arm. Maybe she fancied me and was only allowing her emotions to show how she felt in danger. Maybe she was scared and I could have been anyone or anything she grabbed, but I was sixteen and a woman was touching me.

We took a couple of slight bends down that hill which would have taxed a rally driver, but possibly because of our weight we somehow squashed the car to the road. After a freezing, exhilarating ride, Napoleon started to apply the brakes, and the tyre noise increased as the tread bit into the tarmac. The wind died down and finally we came to a gentle halt. It was pitch black outside, I couldn't make out a thing.

'Keep quiet everyone,' said Napoleon. 'I'll have a chat with the fellow and see what we can do.'

He got out of the car and we heard him walk a short distance and knock on a door. Suddenly a little light came on and we could see we had stopped outside a small cottage which had two petrol pumps on its front wall. Napoleon stood talking to a man wearing a cardigan, who soon touched his forelock, leant back into the house and pulled out a heavy coat. He walked over to the pumps, jangling keys. Napoleon returned to the car and as he rolled it nearer the pumps he whispered back to us, 'He's giving us the petrol. Get down as low as you can and keep quiet.'

We did as we were told and listened as Napoleon spun a tale of how he was from Hereford and had been lent the car by a farmer to visit a family who used to be in his parish but now lived in Builth Wells. It seemed Napoleon was furnishing the poor man with so much information there was never a chance to ask a question. I suppose that was the idea.

As we continued our journey, now with the engine running, there was a heated discussion about whether we should go back at some time and give the man the money for the petrol. This moral dilemma clearly wasn't making Napoleon too depressed. He was on a high. He kept bursting out laughing and repeating the phrase, 'He thought I was a vicar. Vicars get free petrol. I love this costume, man. Brilliant.'

The party was in a large, comfortable, early Victorian country house just outside Builth Wells, the sort with a welcoming, brightly lit entrance lobby smelling of damp wood and wellington boots. There was a huge spread of food on a kitchen table, hundreds of bottles of wine and beer, and a big room, devoid of furniture, ready for dancing.

'Are you from Llanbedr?' asked an attractive woman holding a wine glass, standing in the middle of the dancing room, not dancing. She had a huge frizzy mop of almost black hair, thick and luxuriant, tied off her face with a colourful ethnic scarf of some sort.

'Um, no, I'm from Oxford,' I said, thrilled that I looked as though I lived on a Welsh hill farm.

'What are you studying?' asked the woman. She thought I was a student, she actually thought I had sat and passed my Oxbridge entrance exams and had taken up residence in a medieval college. She thought I was nineteen, when I was only sixteen; she thought I had a posh enough accent to be a student. I was sorely tempted to lie. I wanted to sound like I was really intelligent. I thought of saying I was studying cartoons, but I wasn't sure there was a course in cartoon drawing at Oxford. I thought of saying poetry. In those last few seconds I stood on the edge of an abyss. She had wonderful eyes, she was tall, she was really quite old, probably twenty-eight. She didn't exactly fit my bare-breasted, log-splitting hippie maiden image, but she made my heart beat faster.

'Poetry,' I said. Her eyebrows raised. I knew she would see right through me, and I quickly added, 'But not at university. I just like it, so I study it.'

'You're not at university?'

'No.'

'I see. Sorry, when you said Oxford . . .'

'I just live there.'

She nodded, looked at me intently, silently, as if she had a perfectly natural right to do so.

'Who do you read?' she suddenly asked with a lovely smile. I didn't see this question coming and the smile hit me to the boundary. I'd barely even looked at a book since I was twelve.

'What, poetry?' I said, stalling as best I could. She just nodded silently, locked on to my eyes. I grabbed at the first name that came into my head. 'Hilaire Belloc,' I said. This seemed to throw her.

'Really. He's . . . well, he's very good, for what he does,' she lied.

'Yeah, he's great, but really I'm a cartoonist and an urban peasant.'

'That sounds almost painful,' said the woman. 'What does an urban peasant do in his spare time?'

'I don't have any spare time. Spare time is for people with jobs. I just live,' I said dogmatically.

'Wonderful. So what are you doing here?'

'I hitched up from Oxford today. We just turned up at Llanbedr and then came here. With Napoleon. D'you know him?'

'No, I only know Mary, who lives here.'

'I don't know Mary,' I said.

'She's very nice,' said the woman.

'What d'you do?' I asked her.

'I'm a Jungian analyst,' she said.

'Oh, right,' I said.

'And a professor of poetry.'

'Oh, I see. Right, yeah,' I said, scratching the back of my neck nervously. 'I've read a lot of Hermann Hesse. *The Glass Bead Game, Demian, Steppenwolf.*'

'Really. Well, they're not strictly speaking poetry.'

'No, I mean he's pretty Jungian, isn't he?' I said, my toes curling in the hope that I hadn't muddled Jung with Freud, the sex one with the dreamy, spiritual one.

'Hermann Hesse as Jungian texts, interesting idea. They're very, um, interesting. Did you like them?'

'I suppose so,' I said, wanting to get off the subject. She was clearly going to ask me what they were about, and I couldn't remember a thing about them. I'd read them because Allie had bullied me into doing so.

'I liked the cover of *Demian*,' I said quickly. 'The book cover, I mean. I copied that painting of the face on to the wall in my parents' house.'

'Oh dear, didn't they mind?'

'I was allowed to pretty much do what I wanted in my

own room. My dad's a painter and my mum's a horse breeder,' I lied, lies started to spill out in clots. 'But I've left home now. I live in a commune, in St Bernards Road, opposite the Victoria Arms.' She nodded, knowing where I meant. She didn't ask me anything, she just looked at me over her wine glass.

She said, 'You're very pretty,' at exactly the same time I said, 'What does a Jungian analyst do?'

'Sorry?' I said, trying to get her to repeat what I had clearly heard.

'It doesn't matter,' she said. The moment seemed to have passed, very quickly. Maybe she had decided I wasn't pretty enough to embarrass herself.

'You asked me what a Jungian analyst does,' she said. I nodded, trying to look pretty, no doubt failing. 'I listen to people's dreams, interpret them, help them through their terrors.'

'I see,' I said, transfixed by her velvety softness. 'That's amazing.'

'D'you have dreams?' she asked, leaning a little closer.

'Oh yeah, really intense ones, every night.'

'Repetitive ones?'

'I don't know, they're all different,' I said. 'Mostly they're about sex, in one way or another. And dogs.'

'Dogs,' she said. 'Dogs in dreams are interesting. Dogs are the animal.'

This was when I first caught a whiff of the possibility that this woman was completely barking mad. I'd never studied Jung, in fact I'd barely studied anything since primary school, but I knew from the age of about three that dogs were animals.

'The anima,' she said. 'The wild side.' There was a smile on her lips as she said this. 'Your anima is trying to get in touch with you.'

'Oh brilliant!' I said. This idea fitted in with my theories about really wanting to be a wild man of the hills. Although not quite as wild and dirty as the man I'd met by the fire at Llanbedr.

'D'you know that bloke?' I asked. 'He's a bit wild. He won't live in a house, he lives in a teepee.'

'I can't see him,' she said. We were standing all of six feet from where he was sitting on the floor with the dogs.

'There,' I said. 'On the floor. The very dirty bloke. He's got to be in touch with his animal bit.'

'Anima,' she corrected. 'Listen,' she put a hand on my shoulder, 'there are some people I can't see.' I stared at her. She looked so calm and rational, she was dressed like a rich hippie, comfortable, familiar, yet she kept throwing me with these unexpected statements. I was looking into a world I had no understanding of, no references for. Abbie Hoffman never spoke about the anima; the underground magazines I had bought never discussed dreams.

'I don't understand,' I said, staring into her eyes. I hoped this action would make me seem more intense, more vulnerable, more kissable. I had an intense desire to be held and kissed by this dark woman.

'No, I don't expect you to. It's rather complex. There are just some people I cannot see, I prefer not to see, people who are dangerous, or destructive. I just don't see them. And they don't see me,' she said with a smile. 'Only special people can see me.'

I didn't understand what she was saying, and yet it was a hugely attractive idea. I had been brought up in a spiritually bereft environment. I wanted to find out more about Jung, and dreams, and the other side of my experience that I had no words or even crude tools of understanding for, but which I knew to exist from the effect they had on my waking life.

'D'you live in Oxford?' I asked.

'Yes, I live in residence at Worcester College.'

'Oh, right,' I said. 'At the bottom end of Walton Street. I know it.'

'I've never thought of it like that,' she said.

'Like what?'

'I never thought of the college being at the bottom end of Walton Street. It's very beautiful inside.'

'Is it?' I said, being polite, suddenly feeling I was talking to one of my mum and dad's friends. I wanted to break that feeling. 'Yeah, well, town and gown. You know.'

I'd learned the term 'town and gown' from my friends the urban peasants. It referred to the medieval tradition of animosity between students and townspeople in Oxford. There had regularly been huge riots in the High Street going back to 1357 or something. I was told this by a student in the Victoria Arms one night. I was supposed to be impressed, and I was. I didn't know who'd won the street fights, but I did know who ruled the country thereafter. Not, needless to say, the urban peasants of fourteenth-century Oxenford.

'There's a side of me,' I said, feeling my pulse beginning to race, 'which would like to burn down the poncey colleges, shoot the poncey students and level the whole fucking town. Starting with St John's College.'

'Oh dear,' said the woman. 'And why is that?'

'Because they're so, I don't know, so fucking arrogant. You're not,' I assured her, 'but some of the students I've met, they own everything, they control everything. Did you know you can walk from Oxford to Southampton without ever stepping off land owned by St John's College? They're not a college, they're a property speculation company.'

'You seem very angry about St John's College,' she

said, pulling her head back and away from me a little as though I might strike her.

'They own the squat I was living in. They tore it down.'

'Where was that?'

'Wellington Square.'

'Oh yes,' she said. 'I remember, but they're building a new student accommodation block there, aren't they?'

'Yeah, for bloody students, who've already got more than anybody. It's not fair.'

'Surely saying things aren't fair is the weakest form of argument?' she said calmly.

'But not saying it doesn't make things fair either,' I said, feeling rather proud of the force my anger gave my arguments. 'People are so poor in Oxford. I've seen them. They're treated so badly, and students are so rich.'

'Oh really,' she protested. 'The students I teach are very poor indeed.'

'You don't know what the word poor means,' I said arrogantly.

'Have you ever been to India?' she asked with a cutting edge to her voice. She was getting angry.

'No, can't afford to go.'

'Well, that's a very poor excuse for one thing, and another thing, the people there are very poor indeed. So poor that they drop dead on the streets from hunger. And Biafra, where children starved to death in front of their mothers' eyes. They were poor. If you really want to help poor people, you should go there, or you should do something positive to help them, rather than hanging around here in luxury, complaining about how unlucky you are.'

I pursed my lips. I couldn't argue with her, but I knew she was wrong. I knew I was wrong too. I was angry because I'd blown some sort of chance, I wasn't sure what the chance was, but yet again my anger and hopeless frustration at the world I saw made me destroy an opportunity to enter another world. I walked away from her, left her standing there, feeling more stupid with each step.

'You look glum,' said Jenny, who looked dreadful. She was sitting next to three women in weird face paint who were laughing very loudly and drinking from a bottle of wine.

'Yeah, I just had an argument about Oxford students with that woman over there.' I pointed back to my dark woman who had disappeared. Jenny nodded, not really interested. I remembered about her pregnancy.

'I'm really sorry to hear about all your problems,' I said. She looked at me slightly quizzically. 'You know, with you pregnant and Chris not wanting you to have the baby.'

Jenny's face folded up in pain as I said this, and one of the women next to her put an arm around her shoulder.

'Oh, well done, you prick,' she shouted.

I stood there, feeling tall and skinny and genitally exposed. Jenny sobbed painfully, her shoulders rocking. I shrugged. I couldn't believe that what I had said had come as such a shock.

I looked over to see if I could pick out Chris in the swaying throng of the party. He was easy to spot, and clearly Jenny had been watching him. His hair was bouncing up and down as he danced, his wild man felt-leaves bouncing with him. He seemed completely oblivious of Jenny's pain.

'Jenny, I'm really sorry,' I said, putting a hand on her juddering shoulder. 'I don't know anything, that's just what that weird bloke who lives in the teepee told me. What does he know.'

'He's Chris's best friend!' wailed Jenny.

'Oh, go on,' said the woman with the painted face, 'make it worse!'

I fled for the kitchen, a huge Pickwickian room: a high ceiling complete with hanging herb bunches, a large central table where the food pile had shrunken considerably, wine bottles perched on every available flat surface. All empty. People were talking, kissing, drinking and sitting all over the place. The room was packed, smoky and wonderful. I felt at home again, immediately forgetting what had just happened.

Napoleon was sitting on the kitchen drainer with a dozen people listening to him. I stood nearer.

'We were hitching south, near Hamburg,' he said, his bright blue eyes fixing everyone with their dazzle, 'right out in the middle of nowhere. A camper van stopped and these two guys were driving it, both, like, with really short hair, and we thought, uh-oh, here we go. But they were cool. We got in the back and asked them if they minded if we spliffed up. One of them turned around, and, like, that was the first sign, because he could turn too far. Honestly, we weren't stoned at this time, the guy turned around from the front seat and his head was, like, almost backwards on his shoulder. He looked at us and it was really like, you know, right through. Shooom. Heavy stuff. He just said no, and turned back. Well, me and Dipper were freaked out, man. Heavy, heavy, heavy. We skinned up fast and smoked a spliff.'

A huge, hairy, bearded man entered the kitchen.

'Hey Dipper, man, I'm telling them about the lift.'

'Heavy,' said Dipper, who turned and walked out.

'So there we were, thinking, what the fuck was that, maybe he's just got a supple neck. Then, I was just staring between them, out at the road and, like, the radio just turned on. Neither of them touched it, it was weird. The

67

dial moved up and down without anyone touching the bloody thing. It settled on a music station, a rock station. Hey, Dipper!' shouted Napoleon.

Dipper's head reappeared around the door. 'What?'

'What was the song they played on the radio?'

' "When You're Strange", Doors,' said Dipper.

'Yeah, bloody hell,' said Napoleon. ' "When You're Strange". It was all too much. So then, right, they pull into a service station and the engine just starts to misfire and then runs out of petrol. They knew it was going to, they timed it perfectly. Okay, so that was weird enough, but then, right, the driver gets out and starts to fill the tank, the passenger gets out and sits in the driver's seat. The driver goes and pays the cashier and gets in the passenger seat. The guy in the driver's seat just sits there, doing nothing. Hands down by his sides. Weird, we thought, we were shitting ourselves by now, but we couldn't move. The driver looks at the other guy, just looks at him, and the guy turns the ignition key, but you could see by the way he held it, he'd never done it before. They kept looking at each other as he put it into gear and moved off. The driver wasn't looking where he was going at all. Just staring at the other guy. You know, it was too much, we pulled back on to the autobahn and merged with the traffic, no problem, and I swear to you, I swear, that driver didn't look in front of him for, like, ten minutes. Not once.'

There was a silence from the little group. I was transfixed. Napoleon had done so much: he drove a Land Rover, he'd hitched through Germany, he'd been given lifts by alien beings.

'Were they aliens then?' said a full-faced blonde woman.

'I don't know,' said Napoleon. 'They looked like you

and me, their hands were a bit weird, you know, very long, thin fingers.' He looked at his hand and then said with a poor American accent, 'Dark they were and golden-eyed.'

'Amazing!' I said. 'They must have been aliens then.'

'Why?'

'Because they had golden eyes.'

'No, that's just the name of a science fiction book shop in London, man. It was a joke.'

'Oh,' I said, utterly confused. Dark they were and golden-eyed. It stayed with me.

'Whoever they were,' said Napoleon, 'they were really weird.'

'What happened though?' I asked. 'Did they take you to where you wanted?'

'Yeah,' said Napoleon. 'They dropped us off just outside Munich, on a roundabout, gave us a thumbs up sign, like they'd seen us do when we were hitching, and then disappeared.'

'Wow!' I said. 'What, the camper van, like, disappeared!'

'No,' said Napoleon. 'No, it just drove off, I mean we didn't see them again.'

I felt slightly let down by the down-beat ending, but it was a great story, and one which I added to my repertoire. 'This mate of mine, right, he was hitching . . .'

I managed to build myself a large cheese, hummus and pickle sandwich just before someone shouted, 'It's nearly midnight. Come on, everybody, Auld Lang Syne!'

My hand was grabbed by a tall man next to me. I dropped my sandwich. The crowd in the kitchen formed a circle, linking arms, as more people poured in. The whole party seemed to pile into the kitchen. We didn't form a circle, more a double helix of linked people.

"Happy New Year everybody!' shouted Napoleon who

was looking at his watch. Everybody started kissing. I got kissed by all sorts of people I'd never met before, men, women, children. We seemed to have forgotten the Scottish song which no one knew the words to, but suddenly it emerged from the mass, people linked arms immediately and joined in.

> 'Should old acquaintance be forgot
> and never to de dum,
> should la de da de dum de do
> for the sake of Auld Lang Syne.'

People cheered. I even saw Jenny and Chris embrace. They held each other for a long time; people gave them the room to do so. The velvety Oxford woman was busy hugging another, red-haired woman with remarkable green eyes and freckled skin. I stood close by, hoping she would notice me. She did, and beckoned me over.

'Happy New Year,' she said and kissed me lightly on the lips. 'I don't even know your name.'

'Rob.'

'Hello, Rob. I'm Margaret, this is Mary.'

'Hello, Rob. Happy New Year,' she said and smiled. Then she kissed me too. My mind immediately filled with complex fantasies about living with Mary and Margaret, about having sex with them on dark velvet sheets, of lying, pretending to be asleep, while they discussed my fragile male beauty.

Margaret said something to Mary, they both laughed, and my fantasy disappeared as my blushes increased. There was something so intense about them, some power I felt in their presence. Their eyes looked like the sort that are supposed to see into your soul. Hermann Hesse would have thought they could read the future or something. I didn't actually feel them seeing my soul, but they made me tense. I left the two velvety women, my mind still filled with taut-skinned breasts, freckled forearms and small pieces of ethnic cloth just draped over various nether regions.

People were getting very drunk all around me. I had no desire to join them so I just sipped on a glass of beer for the rest of the night, until Napoleon started to indicate that he was heading back to Llanbedr. It was three in the morning.

I tagged along behind the stumbling throng, toppling over as they tried to pull on their wellington boots and Afghan hats. I stroked one of the dogs, who yawned and shivered by my feet.

Back in the Llanbedr commune I spent the night by the fire, wrapped in an old blanket, head propped up on the filthy seat cushion of the dilapidated sofa. I was kept warm by numerous dogs, half listening to the steady drone of the man who lived in the teepee. I have no memory of what he said, just his constant babbling in the background. It was like listening to the BBC World Service at the dead of night when someone has spiked the water system at Bush House with a psychotropic drug.

One dog in particular seemed to take to me, a lurcher bitch of about three months, all feet and legs and damp quivering nose. She licked my face repeatedly through the long, dark night. She sneezed delightfully when I lit a roll-up made of the tobacco dregs we found in a large glass jar on the mantelpiece.

Rolling up second-hand tobacco, sitting near a fireplace in a Welsh farmhouse commune, the massive bulk of the Black Mountains slowly emerging with the dawning light, surrounded by dogs, listening to a madman who lived in a teepee. I felt like I'd arrived. I'd had a strong experience, something I could tell people about. I had a history, a thing I desperately wanted. I was sixteen years old, mixing with people who had been all over the world, had sex, had children, lived in communes, seen wars, met aliens, lived in teepees. I hadn't done anything except pass my art O level and get thrown out of school. I needed to have done something so I could carry it around with me and not feel so naked.

It was at Llanbedr that I first saw the sign, read a phrase which I managed to use to justify what would eventually prove to be too much. The sign was hand-painted on wood, quite nicely done in a home craft sort of way. It was hanging, dusty, above the door from the big living room into the kitchen. It read:

To live outside the law, you must be honest.

I never forgot that sign, the feeling of strength and certainty it gave me. It stated, in one succinct line, everything I had been struggling to formulate from the age of fourteen when I knew the grown-ups were wrong.

To live outside the law, you must be honest. It made me feel warm inside, it gave me the certain knowledge that other people had found the fit of the society we were brought up in uncomfortable. We had been led to believe it was unchangeable, rigid and the right to alter anything in society was held by an exclusive set. I wasn't sure who they were, but not people I had ever met. It also implied that to live inside the law, you had to be dishonest, a revelation which made a huge amount of sense to me.

'To live outside the law, you must be honest,' I said out loud to the teepee man.

'I made that,' he said. 'It's a quote from Bob Dylan.'

'Is it in a song?' I asked. I adopted my nasal Bob Dylan impersonation, singing the phrase badly.

'No, he just said it, man,' said teepee man without humour.

'It's brilliant though, isn't it? It says everything. Brilliant.'

'I live outside the law,' said the teepee man. 'Very few people do, they're too scared to lose their little trinkets, their little knick-knacks that make them feel safe. It's unsafe outside the law, man. Survival is transcendental. You've got to go with fate, all the way. There's no compromise. All the way.'

Somehow, he managed to make living outside the law uniquely unattractive. He made it sound like a game of rugby, a macho challenge that wimps would balk at. Not an eager and hopeful opening of doors, but a run through a minefield of danger and darkness. I had gone off the teepee man in a big way, but I still suffered from the fact that I utterly believed and agreed with whomever I was listening to, until I heard the next contradictory opinion, when I would realize how wrong that person was and how wise the next turned out to be.

I looked back up at the sign, trying to forget teepee man had painted it. I wanted to do a cartoon story which illustrated the meaning. I fantasized that it was published, that Paul McCartney wanted to make it into a film, that he and Linda would visit me at the little house in St Bernards Road, that they would have a very beautiful young friend, a French girl, and that she and I would live in Paul's big house in Scotland and eat oranges and sleep together in a huge four-poster bed.

I lay under my blanket nursing a comfortable erection, until slowly my thoughts returned to earth and the reality of what lay ahead. I knew I was never going to be in a position to change British society. It would mean at the very least joining the Labour Party, in power at the time and building nuclear power stations, selling arms to foreign dictators and wearing bad suits. It would mean having a hair cut and wearing a tie when I went around door to door canvassing support. It would mean sitting on committees and talking about policy, arguing my case, being overruled. Worst of all, it would mean joining in with something which was already up and running. Having to obey a set of rules made by people I had no respect for. I didn't want to join in with anything.

The weak sun finally made its appearance over the Black Mountains at about 9.30, and a few commune members slowly started to emerge from the warren of upstairs rooms. I made porridge on the large coal-fired Aga cooker in the bitterly cold kitchen. People smoked roll-ups, coughed hugely and grinned at their wonderful lack of health. They pushed their sleep-matted hair out of their puffed-up eyes and said things like, 'I feel utterly fucked.'

At about midday I went for a walk with all the dogs and a handful of people up the hill. The wind was fresh, and my long hair whipped around my head as the grey wisps of cloud shot past feet above our heads.

An old man walked past us with a stick and a sheep dog sticking to his wellington boot.

'You late back last night then?' he asked, his voice a joy of unashamed accent.

'Yeah, we got wrecked, over at the Fisher house in Builth.'

'Oh, that used to be a lovely house,' said the farmer looking up at the hills. 'Now, where are my bloody sheep?'

We looked up the vast expanse of grey-green grassland.

Fifty or so sheep were bounding along together in a pack, for no reason at all that we could make out.

'God, sheep are really, really stupid, aren't they?' I observed.

'Oh no, sonny, they're very advanced, you know,' said the old shepherd gravely. 'You see the way they all turn together up there? See that?'

I watched the flock move like a J-cloth over a draining unit.

'See, they move as one,' he said.

'Yeah, yeah, right,' I said, instantly changing my opinion and agreeing with him.

'You know why that is?' he asked, his thin-lipped face turning into a pleasant grin.

'No,' I said, 'although I lived near a farm before I left home. There were sheep out the back all the time, so I'm sort of used to them.'

'I'll tell you why,' he said ignoring my babble. 'They communicate with each other in ways we don't under-stand. They think collectively.'

'Psychic,' said the man from the teepee.

'I don't know about that, but they think collectively, so they all move as one. They're very much more intelligent than we give them credit for.' He stood looking up at his flock as they moved around the hill like one biological organism.

'Amazing,' I said.

'You daft bugger,' said the farmer, laughing gently. 'Happy New Year to you,' he said and trudged off up the hill.

That night we ate a huge meal together which I helped cook. Sylvie, the Frenchwoman I was nearly in love with, seemed to have taken on the role of mother of the house. Her baby needed feeding and changing, and when I did this without too much fuss, I clearly scored some favour-able points.

'Thank you, Robert. If only some of the other men here were like you.'

I glowed, to be singled out from other men by a beautiful Frenchwoman with a baby. A compliment indeed. I could imagine falling into her warm, musty bed and laughing and talking as we made long, slow love. But there were huge amounts of potatoes to peel and cook, vast arrays of carrots and swede to scrape and chop. Cooking for this many people was a monster process. I was the only man involved, surrounded by women talking, screaming and laughing in the kitchen. True, some men were being useful and chopping firewood or sweeping the incredibly filthy floor, some were holding children or reading the older ones stories, but most were sitting by the fire smoking dope. This didn't fit the picture I had of what a commune should be like. They should be out hunting, or gathering wild moss or something, not sitting there like they were in Oxford, listening to the stereo and smoking dope.

Napoleon walked into the kitchen wearing a long pointy hat with green stripes and with a bell sewn on the end. It was an elfin lord's hat, the bell making the cloth flop over in just the right way. It was the most brilliant hat I had ever seen.

'When's supper, ladies?' he asked with a beaming smile.

'When we have slaved away and cooked it for you,' said Sylvie with a flick of her luxurious hair.

'Marry me, Sylvie,' said Napoleon, 'and I'll take you away from all this.' The other women screamed in delight and derision.

'Yes, you'll take me to another kitchen, give me more babies and then run off with a younger girl,' shouted

Sylvie. This statement raised a cheer from the women, one of whom threw a half-scraped carrot at Napoleon.

'Oh, where's the romance?' said Napoleon. He sat down next to me and munched on the raw carrot he'd caught.

'Don't you live here then?' I asked.

'Me, live in this mad house? You must be kidding,' said Napoleon.

'Is it mad then?'

'You have to be crazy to live here,' said the woman sitting next to me. I had no idea who she was, or where she might live, or if she had any children, or where she came from, but what she said changed the early course of my life. 'It's so untogether and because of the nature of the people here it means the lazy ones, the guys in front of the fire, have a great time. They get stoned, talk all day, get drunk at night and do nothing. We all work really hard trying to keep it together. I'm moving out. I've had enough. Life's hard enough when you're looking after yourself; I don't need to support a bunch of no-hopers like them.'

I nodded. I could just see the edge of the group of men sitting around the fire. They were talking and laughing; there was something about them which reminded me of football teams and rugby clubs. They had no guilt when grouped together, they didn't feel the need to help feed the children or clean the house, wash the clothes or make the garden usable. They just wanted to sit around, get stoned and tell each other daft stories. It was a depressing moment. The place, the farmhouse itself, was so magical, a truly huge house with two staircases, three floors, more rooms than I ever saw, wonderful attics, views from each window to die for, the most idyllic place I'd ever seen. Everything I had dreamed about for years. A commune in the Welsh mountains. I had drawn plans for a school project of a self-supporting community in Wales, with windmills, waterwheels, duck ponds, vegetable gardens, cattle sheds, bicycle repair shop, home-made wine and bread.

Now I was sitting in the kitchen of what passed for a Welsh commune and it was a mess. It was a dysfunctional community, the women were carrying the burden, the children looked filthy and slightly malnourished, everyone signed on and was short of money. Everything was covered in dust and grime, no one had fixed the latch on the back door so the huge pig was constantly invading. It was a picture of dilapidated rural poverty.

It wasn't what I'd expected at all.

'It's really depressing,' I said, looking at the suddenly silent faces of Napoleon and the women. 'I've dreamed about living in a commune for so long, you know, when I was at school, and I studied things about solar power and wind generators and all that, and I come here and it's well, it's . . .'

'A bloody mess,' said Napoleon. 'Here, have my hat.' He pulled the hat off and forced it over my head. 'Happy New Year.'

I stayed at Llanbedr for another five nights before getting a lift back in an unheated Citroën 2CV. I sat next to Jenny, who wasn't crying. Her boyfriend was driving, off to set up a Citroën 2CV workshop in London. He was leaving the commune too. It was over. I was too young to have lived there, I had missed out. They had tried it and failed, they were all going back to living as the rest of the world did, in little families, owning their own washing machines, having everything neat and clean.

6

Brasenose Days

'The college was founded in 1509,' said the bursar in his small white-walled office. 'So we have a system which works rather well, really.' He laughed to himself. 'We've had time to iron out all the wrinkles, you see.'

He kept laughing with his mouth wide open. 'Well, we should have done, with over 500 years' practice!'

His eyes watched me, waiting for me to make a laugh-based response. I'm sure he would have been satisfied with a giggle, a slight snort, even a smirk. But I didn't understand a thing he was going on about and I wasn't in the mood so I stared at him with my eyebrows slightly raised. He finally let out a little sigh and closed his mouth.

For some reason I was expecting his office to be lined with wood panelling, and for there to be an old clock ticking on a mantelpiece. It was certainly old; I had no idea how old, but it was white, with ugly modern furniture. I had expected the bursar to look like one of Mr Pickwick's mates, with tailcoat and breeches, but in fact he was a dull-looking man in a suit, with a white shirt and a dull blue tie.

The man with the even cheaper suit who sat behind the number seven cubicle at the social security office on Marston Ferry Road had given me another piece of grey-brown card containing the address of Brasenose College in his tiny scrawl. 'They are looking for kitchen staff,' he said. 'No experience needed, they'll train you up for all the related duties you'll be expected to perform.' I pondered on what those duties might be. Being stripped naked, covered in oil and masturbated to death by drunken students. Giving oral sex to lecturers, both male and female, on their way to high table. Being gang buggered on a staircase just to pass the time of day. My mind swam with adolescent filth.

I took the card and strolled back into the centre of Oxford with my new companion, a dog called Cabbage. A hippie called Wizard who lived in the Llanbedr commune had given her to me. He preferred to call her Elfin, but somehow the people who called her Cabbage seemed more interesting and so Cabbage she became. I was pretty sure Wizard's real name was Kevin, or Malcolm, since he looked like he came from a new housing estate on the edge of somewhere like Leicester. He had grown his hair long and wore uncomfortable ethnic clothes. He had made me promise to take good care of Cabbage, which I had gladly done.

Cabbage trotted proudly along St Clements, past the busy roundabout and over Magdalene Bridge. It was term time and the place seemed alive with students, bicycles by the dozen flying along the road, buses and cars grinding their way past. At one point, half way across the bridge, Cabbage stopped and sniffed the air. On the opposite footpath a very tall, thin young man was walking along in a floor-length tatty, black cloak. He had a cat sitting on his shoulder. An actual, real cat, well, kitten, a scrotty-looking, grey kitten. There were other oddly dressed individuals around him, wearing half-ripped fur coats, skin-tight black loon pants, ripped and worn, big floppy boots painted silver and red, but none quite so outstanding as the tall thin boy with the cloak. I think one or two of them may have nodded at me, and I nodded back rather shyly.

I turned off the High after I had passed St Mary the

Virgin Church, walked along a narrow cobbled alley and was greeted by the sight of the Radcliffe Camera, a splendid soft stone building whose every shape, curve and carving seemed to exclude me. I didn't even know what it was for.

I wandered round the square, staring at the building, feeling lonely and excluded. It was hard not to. All around me were groups of students walking along together, going somewhere. They were talking earnestly, laughing, some of them even romantically holding hands. They had so much to do. I just had to buy some dog food.

It was impossible for me to wind back far enough into my past and see the possible turn I had taken which meant I was expelled from school at fifteen rather than studying hard and trying to go to university. I had never, until that moment, considered that going to university would be anything other than awful. Having to do as other people told you, having to obey the rules, accept the status quo, have the agenda set for you by an authoritarian master race of knowing old men. That was my angry analysis as I circled the Sheldonian on a grey late-January morning. This bloody building was put up by old men who thought they ruled the world, and for some time they actually had. I hated all of them and decried everything they stood for.

The domed roof of the Radcliffe Camera started me dreaming of setting up my own university, maybe next to Llanbedr, with a huge geodesic dome for a central library, and lecture halls in wooden buildings all along the valley. You could only get in if you had long hair and believed in a total cultural revolution. I could imagine myself walking through the university grounds, and being interviewed by some man in a suit from the BBC who just wouldn't understand what we were doing at the university: there would be no exams; students would set their own time-table; and when they felt they'd learned enough, they'd just leave.

I looked at the little card in my hand: Brasenose College. What a stupid name, it made me think of a shiny metal face, a medieval sculpture of a man with a brass nose. It made me think they'd called it that to keep me out. Where was it? All he said was it would be in the square at the back of St Mary's Church, off the High. The square had three sides which weren't church, they were all high-walled medieval-looking buildings. So which one was Brasenose? There was no sign above any of the doors, there was no indication of any sort. The people who built these places did not want all and sundry to know which was which. You had to be let into that knowledge, some-how. How?

I started walking back the way I'd come, sticking to the walls. Eventually I came to a small gate which was open and I looked in.

There was a sign in the entrance which read, 'Brasenose College is closed to visitors.' I hesitated for a moment, then entered.

'College is closed, you can't bring that in here, son,' said a man with a bowler hat who appeared from an ancient side door.

'I've come to see the bursar bloke, about a job in the kitchens,' I said defensively.

'I don't care if you're the soddin' Dean's nephew. You can't bring a dog in here.'

I went back out through the gate and found a drain-pipe. Cabbage sat down quietly as I lashed her lead to the pipe. I stroked her coarse hair and buried my face in her warm neck. I was not feeling good about this whole enterprise. I wanted to go home to my parents' house and have a cup of tea in their warm living room, and have clean clothes to put on, and not have to worry about getting a job. I wanted to be hitchhiking along a road in the Midwest of America and be picked up by a hippie bus full of proud-breasted women. I wanted to be anywhere but dwarfed by the Radcliffe Camera, in the middle of Oxford on a cold Tuesday morning.

'I won't be long, Cabbage, girl,' I said, and entered Brasenose College.

There is no question about it: within a few short steps in the city of dreaming spires you can leave one world and enter another. Before I walked through that door, students were just people I saw on the streets of Oxford. People with so much to do. My mother had waxed lyrical about tweed jackets with leather elbow patches, cavalry twill trousers and beautiful shoes. But I had no idea where these people lived, how they survived. My first few steps into an Oxford quad were almost religious in their intensity. For a start, even on a dull morning in late January, there is the physical beauty of the place. There is the smell: damp grass, polished wood, warm cooking, pipe tobacco. It smelled to me of comfort, security, room to think; it smelled of privilege. I felt special even though I was only going to work in the kitchens. I didn't want to be a student, I didn't want to do as I was told, but I had never dreamed of the luxury that lay beyond the gates.

The man with the bowler hat at the gate had given me directions.

'Around the quad, through the central gate at the far end, around the next quad and to the right, then through the alley, the covered one, past the JCR, fifth stairway on the right, third door on the left, marked Bursar. Can't miss it.'

I missed it. I missed it again and again. I had no idea what a JCR was. A JCB was a digger, I'd enjoyed drawing one for a project in my art O level class. Those of us not blessed with a university education, (eighty per cent of the population) will need to be told that JCR stands for Junior Common Room. SCR is the Senior Common Room, where the juniors can't go. Immediately I had the sense of a dense web of rules and traditions which surround these colleges, the very names of which I didn't understand. Years of struggle to be exclusive had, since Victorian times, really paid off. The rest of us hadn't a clue what these people were going on about.

Finally, by chance, I saw the bursar's office. I had no idea what to expect, other than that he would be old and weird. I now know that bursars run the joint in Oxford.

'You keep your hands clean. I like that,' said the bursar. I looked down at them. 'Your nails, you keep them clean. I always take that as a sign of honesty.'

'Really,' I said, more out of confusion than sarcasm. My nails were clean, but that must have been a fluke, although I always washed my hands regularly, especially since my sickness before Christmas.

The bursar warmed to his subject. 'You see, Robert, honesty is a very important part of your responsibilities here, should you be hired.'

'That's okay,' I said. 'I believe that to live outside the law, you must be honest.'

The bursar stopped for a moment, his eyebrows slightly furrowed. 'To live outside the law, you must be . . .'

'. . . honest,' I said.

'Yes, what a fascinating concept,' he said. 'Well, we like to live inside the law here in Brasenose. You see, apart from the basic daily kitchen duties, you'll be expected to clean the college silver.'

Not just silver, college silver. I shrugged and nodded. I pondered momentarily on the difference between common or garden silver and college silver.

'But the thing is,' said the bursar who was clearly relishing telling me this, 'the silver in question is priceless. Many of the pieces are hundreds of years old, some given to the college by kings and princes. We have a punch bowl donated by Henry VII.'

'Oh, right,' I said, not sure what my reaction was meant to be and having no clear mental picture of what Henry VII looked like. I had Henry V and VIII pretty well sorted, but VI and VII were a mystery.

'So, to clean the silver, you'd be locked in a room and unable to leave the premises until the job was done.'

I nodded, not quite believing what I was hearing. This place really was in another century. 'That's okay,' I said. 'I wouldn't try and steal anything; it's against everything I believe in.'

'That's good, that's very good,' said the Bursar. 'Well, when could you start?'

My heart stopped. I had been going to the odd job interview on a regular basis, at electronics companies, clothes shops on the High Street, Woolworth's store room on Cornmarket. I had never been offered the job and it never occurred to me that someone might actually suggest that I start work.

'I, um, I don't know,' I said.

'Well, what are you doing now?'

'Now?' I asked incredulously. 'Well, I've got to go and buy some dog food from the covered market. I've just been given a dog, and I don't like feeding her tinned food.'

'Quite so, but you could go and meet Mr Willis, the head kitchen porter, and have a look around the college.'

He picked up his phone. 'Mr Willis could show you around and give you an idea of what you'd be doing here.'

'All right,' I said, not able to come up with a reasonable excuse but fighting a terrible desire to run for it. The bursar exchanged jocular in-house terminology with Mr Willis. He looked at me and laughed, and I was sure the weird sexual initiation was coming up at any moment.

When he put the phone down I stood to leave. 'Don't you want to know what we pay you?' he asked with a big grin.

'Oh, yes. Of course. Sorry,' I said.

'Well, it's basic thirty-eight pence an hour, with a special overtime rate of fifty pence an hour for things like grand dinners at High Table, college balls and large summer functions, et cetera. How does that sound?'

'It's okay,' I said, nodding. He nodded back and we nodded to each other in silence for a moment. I think he knew at that moment that he was staring across a fairly huge gulf of time and understanding. He and I lived in very different worlds which only overlapped each other physically. I was sent off to meet Mr Willis.

'Left at the bottom of the stairs, around the quad, don't walk on the grass,' said the bursar with his big open-mouthed laugh, 'then through the low archway with the statue above, along the cloister, up the stone steps, through the archway, turn right along the path, down the steps, through the door marked kitchen, along the corridor and it's the fifth door on your left. Mr Willis's office.'

Mr Willis was a far calmer person than the manic bursar. He sat in a small cluttered office off a corridor which smelt of cabbage and a rich liqueur. I stood awkwardly by the door for a while as he finished writing something in a large cash book.

'You worked in kitchens before?' he asked after a while.

'Not really. I'm a cartoonist.'

There was a pause as he wrote something. Then, without looking up, he said, 'What's that then?'

'You know, strip cartoons, like in the papers, like comics,' I explained.

'Is that what you do then?'

'Yes.'

'What you doin' here then?' he asked flatly.

'Well, the dole say I've got to get a job, so they sent me.'

'D'you want to work here?' he asked, now actually looking at me for the first time. I shrugged my shoulders. 'You sound like a fresher. Is this some sort of joke?'

'No. What's a fresher?' I asked.

'Freshman, first-year student,' he said.

'Me, a student!' I said. 'No, no, I've been sent here by the bloke at the Nash office on Marston Ferry Road.' I showed him the grey-brown card with the scrawled address.

'How old are you?'

'Nearly seventeen.'

'Why aren't you at school then?'

'I dropped out. Well, I was expelled. Well, I left, and I live in a commune now, in Wales, Llanbedr. Except we have this system where some members of the commune have to live in the city to earn money for the rest of them, who live out there.'

'A commune.'

'Yeah, it's this massive farmhouse out in the middle of Wales, half way up a mountain. So I've been living there for, like, well, months and months.' I quite liked the feel of this lie so I ran with it. I had actually stayed in Llanbedr for five nights, but Mr Willis wasn't to know that.

'We had a vote, and we decided that three of us had to come to Oxford and get jobs, and then plough the money back into the commune, so we can afford to buy horses to pull the carts and ploughs and that, because we've completely rejected modern farming methods and just want to go back to traditional methods of transport and food production.'

Mr Willis stood silently watching me. I could tell he was lost and no idea what to make of my rambling.

'So in a sense I have worked in a large kitchen before. I can cook for like thirty or forty commune members. It's a bit like a kibbutz, you know, a big canteen type thing we've built on the end of the farmhouse. It's a steel-braced geodesic dome, eighty feet high, underfloor heating. It's low impact technology though. So, yeah, we take turns at cooking and most of the food is home grown and all of it is organic, and we barter with other communes in the valley. It's all pretty well organized.'

Mr Willis stood up and left the room without taking his eyes off me. I followed him down the corridor.

'Not that the way you do food is the same, I'm not suggesting that I cook big organic veggie pies here or anything. It's probably all venison and rabbit and big cows' tongues and pigs' heads with oranges and stuff like that,' I said as I saw a huge noisy kitchen behind him. 'I don't mind about that because I'm not a vegetarian.'

'This is the main kitchen,' said Mr Willis after taking a deep breath. 'You won't be going in there except to pick up trays of food during High Table and what have you. This room here,' he continued down the long stone-floored corridor, opened a door to a room with three enormous stainless steel sinks along one wall, 'this room is where you'll be kept busy most of the time.'

'What happens in here?' I asked innocently.

'Washing up,' said Mr Willis. 'And mind you don't break anything.'

'I won't,' I said. I felt strangely at home in this room, it felt like mine. 'Okay, when do I start?'

'Tomorrow morning, six o'clock sharp.'

'Six o'clock!' I said incredulously. I hadn't got out of bed before ten thirty since I last went to school nine months previously.

'That's when we start laying tables,' said Mr Willis.

'Is there something special going on?' I asked, imagining a visit by a head of state or something equally grand which warranted a special effort by the staff.

'Breakfast,' said Mr Willis flatly.

7

High Table

'So you've started working for a living, have you, Rob the cartoonist?' said Roger in the noisy bar of the Victoria Arms on St Bernards Road.

'Yeah, it's okay really,' I said. 'It's pretty boring, just washing up and clearing up all the rubbish they leave behind.'

'So really you're Rob the washer-up, not Rob the cartoonist,' he said with a wide grin. I smiled and nodded in agreement.

'Yeah, like you're Roger the window cleaner,' I said. There was a silence at our table, the din of the bar, 'Layla' playing endlessly on the juke box. Roger looked at me flatly for a while, then grinned again. 'Cheeky boy,' he said. 'Now you're working, you can buy me a drink.'

I bought my first round of drinks that evening. About seven pints of beer, three of cider and two or three shorts. It cost me half of my first week's wages, which came to the grand total of £15.20. I was rich.

'So, now you've got a job, Rob the washer-up, you can find a woman,' said Roger.

'Oh, and why's that?' I asked.

'That's what you do now you've got a job: toe the line, do as you're told. Get paid at the end of the week. Be a good boy and you get a treat. Pussy.'

'Oh, right,' I said, not having heard the pussy theories for a while.

'Then you'll have a kiddie, then you'll have to keep working for the rest of your life, then you'll die before you retire and just as you gasp your last breath you'll think, "What was that all about?"'

I shrugged. I thought Roger was going a bit loopy, but I saw Gary and Steve nodding sagely.

'Yeah, watch yourself, young Rob,' said Steve. 'Don't settle down too soon. How old are you?'

'Sixteen.'

'You shouldn't have a job,' said Gary. 'You're too young.'

'Well, they only give me £4 a week on the dole, and they stopped giving me that because they thought I should be at school.'

'They've got you by the short and curlies, haven't they, Rob? Get a job, earn some money, spend it, work more. It's a great way to live.'

'No, it isn't and I won't do it for long. I'm just going to save up enough to build a huge geodesic dome at Llanbedr and then I'm going to start up my own university. A free university without all the shit that goes on here.'

Roger, Gary and Steve laughed; they laughed loud and strong, but I could see Gary didn't really enjoy laughing at me this much. Roger, on the other hand, was roaring with genuine cruel mirth.

I got slightly drunk that night, felt very ill and when I lay down to sleep, I had a strong sensation of being on a big wheel that was on the downward spin of its rotation, for ever. Smoking dope never made me feel like this, dope before bed meant I was plagued by intense sexual fantasies. Drink made me feel sick.

When I got up to go to work in the dark the next morning, I realized there was another reason why I didn't like alcohol. I felt awful, with a pounding head, dry mouth, and eyes which really didn't function. Cabbage's marvellous wake-up tail wag was a blur to me as I stumbled through the icy blackness to Port Meadow for her early morning constitutional. When I got back to the cold little house, Gary, Helen and baby Daisy hadn't even stirred. I gave Cabbage a bowl of milk, fussed her as I pulled on the woollen gloves my mum had knitted me and left the house.

I rode my bike the short distance into town, locked it up inside the back gate of Brasenose and started hauling out the breakfast things from the kitchen into the JCR.

'Good morning,' said a haughty voice as I returned to the kitchen across the small quad. 'Hail fellow well met and all that.'

'Sorry?' I said, not sure if he was talking to me.

'You're new here, aren't you?' said the young man wearing baggy shorts and a thick pullover. 'How d'you do? Name's Duncan. Who are you?'

'Robert,' I said.

'Jolly good show, Robert. And, er, how is it going?'

'What?' I said through the fug of my first hangover.

'Breakfast. I'm starving, just been out for a constitutional run, all the way round the grounds of All Souls. Got to keep fit, eh?'

'I don't know. I feel dreadful,' I said, assuming that would be an end of this unexpected encounter. No one other than the staff had spoken to me before. If anything, since my arrival at Brasenose, the students had seemed even more remote than when they walked past me on the street.

'Oh dear,' he said. 'What seems to be the matter, Robert?' I was impressed he could remember my name, I'd already forgotten his.

'Hangover,' I said. 'I was in a bit of a rough pub last night. Got a bit pissed.'

'How terribly exciting,' said Duncan. 'A rough pub. My goodness. Did you get into any bother?'

'No,' I said. 'I'm mates with all of them. I mean, they're nice enough as long as you don't cross them.' As I spoke, this crowd of villains started to emerge from the mist of my imagination. Surly thugs who were my friends and who would terrify ordinary mortals.

'So where is this rough pub?' asked Duncan. 'On the Blackbird Leys council estate, no doubt.' He laughed deeply.

'No. Viccy Arms, St Bernards Road.' Duncan looked none the wiser. 'North Oxford,' I said. 'Just on the corner of Walton Street.'

'Walton Street!' said Duncan excitedly. 'That's not terribly far away, is it? My God, the Visigoths are at the gates! Sound the alarm, et cetera.'

'I don't know,' I said. 'I live right opposite.'

'I'll have to drop in one night. Would you mind?' he asked.

'Don't know,' I said, nonplussed by the question. 'It's not my pub. You can do what you like.'

'Oh, is that an invitation?' asked Duncan. I looked at him and laughed. I really wasn't sure why this strange young man was talking to me. He didn't fit my idea of what a homosexual looked like, and yet there was an immensely strong sexual tone to everything he said, a sort of drag-boys-up-to-his-bedroom-at-his-parents'-house-and-fiddle-about-with-them jollity which I had come across with various boys at school.

I still didn't know how you spotted a homosexual. I refused to go along with the absurd *It Ain't Half Hot Mum* screaming campness which is how most ignorant heterosexuals viewed gay men then. I had seen the Tom of Finland book in Philip and Hilary's flat on Richmond Road. There was not one limp wrist amongst them, just big cowboys in tight jeans with moustaches. This man just looked like a sixth former gone to seed.

'Yeah. I'll meet you there if you want,' I said. 'I'm in there most nights.'

'Excellent,' said Duncan and slapped me on the back. I smiled and walked back into the kitchen.

'He's a fuckin' prize bum bandit, that one,' said Terry, the worrying member of the kitchen staff who'd been in the navy and had rather too many tattoos. He also had a quiff of gravity-defying proportions: a heavily greased Teddy boy quiff haircut with a wrap-over duck's arse at the back and long sideburns on his cheeks, which he constantly referred to as 'buggers handles'.

He must have grown and styled this haircut as a teenager in the late fifties and would continue to wear it that way until his body was dropped into a wooden box.

''Ere, Robert,' he called to me as I stumbled away down the corridor. 'Want to know what I done this mornin'?'

'Um, I'm not sure,' I said, becoming familiar with Terry's obsessions.

'I dropped a turd. Massive fucker it was. It were so big, I had to bend the bastard with a crowbar to get it to flush.' He was enthused by my fit of laughter. 'It was lurching out of the water, trying to bite me,' he added, grinning wildly.

This foul image caused me to laugh uproariously even though the effort brought on acute head pain. Terry was gross and disturbing to be near: he rarely mentioned anything which wasn't connected to his anal passage, what came out of it and what he was convinced that eighty per cent of the student body wanted to shove into it.

I spent the next fifteen minutes making toast in the kitchen. I had started as a kitchen hand, washing up, cleaning the extractor fan filters, slopping down the tiled floor, the most rudimentary and mindless of tasks. As I did them, I would say things to myself like, 'The brain screams in pain as the minutes tick past so slowly it's impossible to record the change.'

I felt I was wasting my time working in the kitchens. I was convinced there was an awful lot happening all around me, just beyond the wall, just beyond the gate. An awful lot was going on and I was missing all of it. I was selling my time to the bursar for £15 a week and I was going nowhere.

By my second week I had been elevated to the dizzy heights of toast manufacturer. Apart from toasting the bread, I had to change out of my clothes and into a simple sort of uniform the college provided: black trousers and shoes, white shirt, black tie. I had to have my hair tied back in a pony-tail. I felt absurd in these clothes, like an off-duty policeman.

In a corner of the kitchen were two big stainless steel catering toasters. The routine was simple: four slices apiece, shove it in, twist the timer knob, read Terry's copy of the *Sun*, respond to the girl on page three with a shocking erection that appeared like an emergency life belt in a plane. Do not pull cord until you are clear of door. Phumth, and there it is, blown up in a second.

'Don't burn the toast, Robert,' Mr Willis would say from down the corridor. He must have been able to smell burning toast from 500 yards.

'Sorry, Mr Willis,' I shouted, smiling at Terry as he passed carrying some empty trays.

'Burn the fuck out of it,' he said. 'It's good for you, burnt toast, makes your crap more solid.'

I had to butter the toast myself, not catering marge at Brasenose but real butter. 'Why can't they spread their own butter, Terry?' I asked as he passed me again, carrying the same trays. He grimaced, lifted one leg and released a noisy and noxious fart.

''Cos if you gave 'em butter they'd use it to lubricate their arses so they could shag each other.' He left the kitchen, then popped his head around the door. 'Or shag me more likely, fuckin' turd burglars the lot of them.'

The contrast between Terry and his toilet-wall consciousness, and the rather fey, pale and twitching young men and women who took one or two slices of toast in the morning couldn't have been more marked. I felt I belonged to neither group and in many ways I felt sorry for both. There was something tragic about Terry's terrible resignation to his position. He was clearly one of the men who went over the top in the First World War, didn't complain, thought their superior officers were wankers and 'turd burglars' but would never challenge their authority, and had their bodies pounded and ripped to death for absolutely no reason.

The students I felt less sorry for, but I was occasionally surprised at myself when the sight of a pale-faced, mop-haired nineteen year old talking to himself in the queue stirred some feelings of pity in me. Some of them seemed to be suffering so much, their mouths and cheeks twitched involuntarily, they chewed their long, delicate fingers. They seemed very nervous, looking at me with a guilty glance as I replenished the toast plate, the only task I was allowed to do in their presence. Other students, better looking, better fed, less twitchy, clearly did not register my existence, talked and laughed loudly, grabbed what they needed in the unconscious knowledge that more toast would always be there in the morning. Things like toast just happened. Many generations ago they had lost all touch with the effort, planning and timing which went into supplying them with a posh plate piled high with pre-buttered toast every morning.

'The silver,' said Mr Willis, standing with his hands on his hips.

'Yeah,' I said, eyebrows raised, waiting to hear what he had to say. Half of what I washed up each day was silver: dozens of tankards with dates stamped on the bottom. 1644. 1728. They were battered and bent but they still held fluid.

'Bursar tells me you are willing to clean it.' Then I remembered what the bursar had said. There must be more silver.

'Yeah, sure, I'll clean it if you want,' I said. 'Don't I have to be locked up or something?'

'No, no, locked *in*, boy, for your own safety. The silver is worth many hundreds of thousands of pounds.'

'Wow, amazing,' I said.

'It's a big job. It could take a couple of days.'

'A couple of days! How much is there?'

'Carry this,' he said, tapping a large cardboard box with his shoe, 'and follow me.'

I picked up the box, relieved to find out it wasn't very heavy, and followed Mr Willis out of the washing-up galley, past Terry, who was possibly masturbating into a large cooking pan, although he could just as well have been cleaning it in an unusual way. We left the building by the low door and walked across the small garden and into the JCR. The room was full of talk and rock and roll on a stereo and students and smoke and long hair. One man stood at the far end, his tight black curls and dark skin marking him out from the rest. He shouted some-thing at someone unseen; he was angry. We walked past briskly and through an oak door set into the corner. I wished I could have stayed a little, joined in maybe. They were talking animatedly, and I heard the words 'fascist' and 'Israel' mentioned in strained, angry voices. This was a group of students I hadn't seen before; they didn't come and eat toast in the morning like the twitchy ones or the posh ones. These students looked more like me: scruffy clothes, long hair, beads and bracelets.

I followed Mr Willis up a flight of wooden stairs, past an open door with a picture of Che Guevara pinned on it, the familiar smell of hash smoke filtering out, mixed with that of wood polish and musty carpet. We went through a smaller oak door and up a narrow flight of stairs. At the top there was a very small oak door; this one looked seriously old, like a medieval door in an ancient castle. It had big black rivets and huge iron hinges, the planks were thick and worn. Mr Willis produced a set of large keys, unlocked the door, and stepped inside.

What greeted my eyes when I entered the room is hard to describe, an array of silver so enormous it deceived the eye. Silver plates the size of children's beds, silver teapot-like things the size of milk churns. Silver candlesticks the size of standard lamps.

'Fucking hell!' I said.

'I beg your pardon, boy,' said Mr Willis.

'I'm sorry, but you know, it's a lot of silver,' I said, touching an odd-shaped thing that looked a bit like a giant gravy boat. 'I've never seen anything like it.'

'There isn't anything like it,' said Mr Willis with a half-smile of pride. 'Now, I'm putting you in a position of the utmost responsibility. Cleaning the college silver is a great honour. It's a difficult job, it needs to be done gently. A little cleaning fluid on the soft grey cloth, a good, firm but not violent buffing with the yellow cloth. Have you got that?'

'Grey for polish, yellow for shine,' I said, smiling and

trying to put him at his ease. He nodded uneasily and contemplated smiling back. He didn't.

'The silver on this table here is to be done first as that has to decorate High Table.' He pointed out a vast array of massive silver items piled on to one groaning folding table set beneath the ancient beams of the roof. 'I suggest you start cleaning the pieces at the far end, and place the polished pieces here,' he pointed to a smaller table near the door which was piled up with old papers, 'until it's full, then transfer the polished items to the empty area at the back of the table, working forward piece by piece.'

'Yeah, okay,' I said, suddenly feeling sorry for Mr Willis. I wondered if this had once been his job, one which he adored doing, and which, due to the pressures of running the catering services in the college, he was no longer able to do. As he picked up a silver and gold goblet, I felt sure I was right.

'This piece dates from 1590, part of a set given to the college by the Archbishop of Canterbury in 1611. Do you know who the Archbishop of Canterbury was then?' he asked. I shook my head. Mr Willis smiled and placed the goblet back on the table. 'Yes, well, there you go.'

'Who was it?' I asked innocently. Mr Willis flashed me an angry look.

'Wouldn't you like to know, boy,' he said, nodding, clearly indicating he hadn't a clue either. I stood in silence for a while taking in the long, low room. Mr Willis fell silent too, letting his hands run over the solid pieces of metal. My forehead had gone tingly and fuzzy as I watched Mr Willis finger the raised emblems and patterns on a silver dish with an ornate lid.

'Beautiful,' he said, 'beautiful.' He sighed and walked to the door. He checked his watch. 'Ten thirty now. I'll come and check on you in a couple of hours.' So saying, he left me in this treasure trove of uncountable millions with a cardboard box of cloth and polish.

I started to clean the silver, pouring fluid on to the grey cloth and rubbing it over the huge heavy objects. I sat on a small medieval-looking stool and rubbed the soft warm metal.

We are simple creatures, or I was at sixteen. The cloth, the raised relief designs on the silverware, the way they bumped gently under my fingers, the whole experience grabbed hold of my brain and groin and pointed me in one direction. The room was strangely warm and within ten minutes of Mr Willis's key turning the lock, I was running through various Tom of Finland-style fantasies mixed in with a healthy dollop of Penthouse Pet-inspired heterosexual musings.

'Too slow,' said Mr Willis at 12.30 when he opened the door. I was busy trying to clean the intricate fretwork on a sort of filigree silver bucket.

'I've done quite a bit,' I said, looking with pride at the shining silverware on the smaller table.

'I'd have done half of it by now,' Mr Willis said, confirming my theories about him. He inspected the silver I'd cleaned. 'Not bad, not bad, but you'll have to get your skates on this afternoon. I want this lot done by nightfall.'

'Yeah, all right,' I said, suddenly feeling the tension in my bladder. 'Now I really need to go to the toilet, Mr Willis,' I said as I moved pass him.

'Ah-ah,' he said, blocking my path. 'I have to check you first.'

'Sorry?' I asked, unclear as to what he meant.

'I'll have to pat you down to make sure you haven't made off with any of the silver.'

I laughed. 'Look at the size of it!' I said. 'Where would I stuff any of it?'

'That's not the point,' said Mr Willis, who very quickly patted me under the arms and down the legs. He held his head far away from me as he did so, clearly not enjoying it. Then he stood up and straightened his cheap jacket.

'Okay, off you go, boy.'

I went down the stairs and opened the door at the bottom. The door with the Che Guevara poster on it was still open, and two men with very long hair and a woman with short hair were hanging around the entrance.

'Hi,' said one of the men, who also had a beard.

'Hi.'

'What's up there?' asked the woman. 'I've often wondered.'

'About ten million quid's worth of silver,' I said. 'I've just been locked in for the past three hours, cleaning it.'

'Oh, what! They locked you in!' said the man with no beard.

'The fascists! That's outrageous,' said the woman.

'Typical fascist behaviour,' said the man with the beard.

'This place is founded on fascism,' said the beardless man. 'Look what happened in the war.'

'Yeah, right,' said the bearded man. Mr Willis came out of the door and locked it carefully. He ignored me completely as he walked stiffly down the narrow passage and disappeared down the stairs.

'Fascist!' said the man with no beard.

'What happened in the war?' I asked. They looked at me, surprised. It seemed they had already forgotten I was the victim of the latest piece of fascist oppression.

'Oxford was never bombed, yeah,' said the man with no beard.

'Wasn't it?' I said, surprised. After all the stories I'd heard about bombing, I assumed everywhere had been bombed. It was part of my childhood.

'Never, not one bomb,' said no beard. 'Coventry, obliterated. Birmingham, London, Liverpool, all bombed to bits. But not Oxford, and yet it was one of the biggest armament-producing towns in the country, because Morris cars — Cowley, just up the road — were making tanks then, not cars, and Hitler never allowed the *Luftwaffe* to bomb it.'

'Yeah, because of the dons, who are all fascists,' said the man with the beard.

'Always have been, always will be,' said the woman.

'Yeah,' said beard, 'the dons did a deal with the Führer, right, directly, with Adolf Hitler, right. They said, "Don't bomb us, and when you win the war, which you will 'cos we'll help you, when you win, yeah, we'll supply you with the top brains to run your super state. Right. No Jews, no homosexuals, no blacks, right. The, like, Aryan élite of the world, nurtured right here."'

'Oh, wow! Amazing!' I said. 'How d'you know?'

'Oh, come on!' said the woman with the hint of a sneer at the corner of her mouth. 'It's bloody obvious, isn't it? This place is the breeding ground of future fascists to replace the likes of Heath and Keith Joseph.'

'I suppose so,' I said.

'Are you in the IMG?' asked the man with no beard.

'What's that?' I asked.

'It's just that I thought I saw you at a meeting.'

'International Marxist Group,' said beard.

'Oh, right,' I said. 'Yeah, IMG. No, I think all political parties are fascist. Whoever you vote for, they always get it.'

'Well, that's really, really naïve,' said the woman. 'That's the best way to support the status quo.' I was knowledgeable enough not to assume she meant the band, but only just.

'Don't you think,' she continued, her eyes locked on me, 'that the oppressed people in the world need some support? Don't you think there needs to be an internationalist agenda, from right now, to support armed struggle, worldwide? To overthrow the war lords and fascist boss classes? Or d'you think they should just put up with it?'

'No, no, of course I think they should all be liberated,' I said, with vague pictures of Africans and Central Americans swimming through my mind, 'totally liberated from all the shackles and that. I've done a cartoon of a sort of half man, half pigeon, breaking out of the pigeon hole, you know, signifying being oppressed, and breaking free, so I really, really think people are oppressed.'

'Yes, but what are you prepared to do about it? Drawing cartoons isn't going to help,' said the woman.

'Art is one of our strongest weapons,' said no beard.

'Oh, what a wanker's thing to say!' said the woman with a cruel laugh.

'Michelle,' said the man with the beard, putting a hand gently on her arm.

'No, fuck it!' she said, wrenching her arm free with a violent jolt. 'You fucking liberationists are all the same. There has to be a hard-line Marxist analysis of what's happening or the cultural hegemony will blind us and we're screwed to repeating the same old mistakes, again and again.'

She stormed off down the stairs and we heard the door slam.

'She's a really heavy chick,' I said.

'Well, she's a Stalinist,' said no beard. 'I can see her point but, you know, sometimes she just gets so mad.'

'She keeps a snake,' said beard.

'Wow!' I said. 'What, like in her rooms?'

'No, she won't live in college,' said beard. 'She says it's too cushy and she wants to live with the working classes.'

'Yeah, she lives off Cowley Road, sort of the wrong side of Cowley Road,' said no beard.

'With a snake?' I said, fascinated by the image this conjured up. I had never met a woman who seemed less sexual before. Up till that point I had judged every woman I met on a purely sexual level: either I fancied them or I didn't. Snake woman was beyond sexuality. She was frightening, clever, quick, angry and worrying. I had no way of telling if what she said was right, or even if what she said made any sense at all. I'd heard of Stalin, but didn't know who he was or what he'd done.

No beard touched my forearm gently. 'But listen, if you've done some cartoons, well, we'd be interested to see them, for the magazine.'

'Oh, wow. D'you publish an underground mag?' I asked, enthused beyond belief.

'It's not really underground, it's more mainstream. We're aiming it at a wider readership,' said no beard.

'Yeah, right, it's called *Unite and Fight for Workers Rights!*,' said beard.

I stared at them for a moment. 'That's the title?' I asked.

'Yeah,' said beard. 'It's got an exclamation mark after it.'

'Right,' I said, fearing, as always, that I was missing the point. 'Well, I've got quite a few drawings already. I had some published by *Carfax Comic*.'

'Oh, no! That bunch of non-aligned anarcho-syndicalist no-hopers!' said beard.

'Yeah, well, you know, I didn't have that much to do with them,' I backtracked. 'I could do more if you wanted.'

'Fantastic,' said no beard. 'Where are your rooms?'

'What? Sorry?' I said, nonplussed.

'Your rooms. Where are you?'

'Oh,' I said, as the penny dropped with a delightful ring. 'I'm not a student.'

'You're not? asked no beard with a look of utter confusion on his face.

'No,' I said. 'I work here. In the kitchens. And up there, cleaning the silver.' I gestured towards the medieval ceiling. The two younger men looked at each other.

'Oh, right,' they said. 'Right. Okay.'

'D'you want to see my cartoons though? I don't live far away. In St Bernards Road. Near the Viccy Arms. I could bring them in tomorrow.'

'Oh, right, well, you see, the magazine is really, well, it's for students,' said no beard. 'It's sort of set up and run by students. We'd have to take it to the publishing executive committee to see what they thought about bringing in outsiders.'

I bit my lips and nodded. Another opportunity to find a publisher doomed. 'Okay,' I said. 'Well, if you want to find me, my name's Rob the Cartoonist and I work in the kitchens.'

'Where's that?' asked beard.

'The kitchens. You know, where they cook all the food,' I said. 'Out of the JCR and straight across the quad. You can't miss them really.'

'I must say I've never been aware of them before,' said no beard.

'Oh, I knew they were there,' said beard. 'I've talked to some of the workers in there. Terry. D'you know him?'

'Yeah,' I said. 'Total fascist.'

'Oh, d'you think so?' said beard. 'I thought he was a classic example of a member of the working-class intelligentsia who has never been given a chance to shine.'

'Oh. Yeah, right,' I said, brow furrowed with crossed lines. 'But, like, a working-class fascist.'

'Maybe,' said beard, looking into the middle distance. There was a heavy silence, and I shuffled uncomfortably. 'Well, I've got to go and get some lunch. I've got to clean more silver this afternoon.' I hoped someone would sympathize with my plight, at least call someone a fascist, but nothing happened. I started walking away and the two men went into the room with the picture of Che Guevara on the door and I never saw them again.

'Hello, Robert,' said Duncan, standing sheepishly close to me as I talked to Cosher Richards in the Victoria Arms early one evening. It was several days since the silver cleaning day, and life had passed along uneventfully. I was due to babysit for Gary and Helen that night, and had just popped into the pub to buy some tobacco. Cosher had offered me a drink, and I was supping on half a draught Guinness feeling comfortable when I heard his voice.

'Hi,' I said, taking a moment to recognize him. He was wearing, almost to the letter, the classic student uniform: duffel-coat and scarf, corduroy trousers, black lace-up shoes, blue and white striped shirt under a green crew-neck pullover.

'Can I get you a drink?' he asked, slowly easing his way between me and Cosher. This was no bad thing because Cosher was rather dull, a completely bald, tattooed lunatic who frequented the Viccy Arms and was reputed to have head-butted someone to death.

'No, I'm okay thanks. I'm babysitting tonight, actually. I can't stop long.'

'Oh, right you are,' said Duncan. 'Well, I'll just have a quick one.'

He bought half a bitter and we sat down at one of the

small circular tables that littered the badly lit, cold and unwelcoming room that was the public bar. The only decoration was a caricature of the publican and his wife, done in that odd, huge-head, small-body style that no one knows who started or why it should be considered popular.

'I missed you today,' said Duncan. 'I didn't make it to breakfast, and that seems to be the only time you're around.'

'Oh, I'm there all bloody day,' I said, 'but I'm only allowed out at breakfast, to do the toast. Terry used to do it.'

'Terry. He's rather awful, isn't he?' said Duncan.

'He's all right,' I said. 'He's just a member of the working class who hasn't been given any chance to shine, like the working-class intelligentsia.'

Duncan stared at me with a half open-mouthed smile.

'He's just really, really messed up by the system,' I explained.

'Oh, what system is that?'

'You know, the system, the stuff, the government, everything. The system.'

'I didn't know there was a system; it's always seemed rather chaotic to me,' said Duncan, trying to roll a cigarette and failing. I rolled one for him and he took it carefully.

'They want you to think it's chaotic,' I said, nodding sagely.

'Do they?' said Duncan.

'Yeah, can't you see that? You guys don't seem to be able to see that.'

'Who are we?' asked Duncan, smiling.

'Students,' I said, as though it was obvious. 'You've copped in for the whole big lie thing. The system.' I was trying to remember all the things Roger had said on those drunken evenings across the road after the pub had shut. He was always going on about how faith was false and how people had faith in things which always let them down.

'You've still got faith in the system, but it will always let you down,' I said.

'Right,' said Duncan, still smiling. 'You've thought about this a lot, haven't you.'

'Yeah, man,' I said. 'You've got to. But really, there's, there's a sort of really, really complex system, keeps us all in our pigeon holes and, well, I've done this cartoon where one person breaks out of their pigeon hole and the result is that because they see that, the other people I mean, see that this one person has broken out, then they all start to break out.'

'A cartoon,' said Duncan.

'Yes. I'm a cartoonist. Well, when I'm not washing up at Brasenose. Yeah.'

'That's amazing,' said Duncan.

'Well, I haven't had much published yet. *Carfax Comic* printed some stuff years and years ago.' I wanted to sound older, as though everything had been done before and I was tired of it all.

'I've seen a *Carfax Comic*,' said Duncan slowly. 'Yes, I bought one a while back, from a chappie with a beard, outside Woolworths.'

'Hugo,' I said nonchalantly. 'He's an anarchist. He knows all the guys in the Angry Brigade,' I said, carefully pronouncing the word brigade.

'An anarchist. How very Viennese,' said Duncan with a yawn.

'Sorry?' I said.

'Viennese. Anarchists always make me think of Vienna.

You know, chaps with cloaks running through the streets at night carrying bombs which look like black Christmas puds. With the word bomb written on them.'

I nodded. There was a silence.

'So, um, when did you have something in *Carfax Comic*?'

'Last year,' I said, now slightly embarrassed that he might have seen it.

'Oh, what was the cartoon?'

'Well, there was an exploding planet on the cover,' I said, 'and inside there was this single cartoon drawing of a vicar.'

'Yes!' said Duncan. 'Oh, rich. Truly rich.'

The cartoon he was referring to depicted a vicar kneeling with his trousers pulled down, masturbating over some open pornographic magazines. A man had appeared in a doorway behind him and had a speech bubble which read, 'Vicar, I loved your sermon on the evil of pornography and the importance of the Festival of Light . . . oops!'

'It's filthy!' said Duncan a little too loudly. The motley clientele of the Victoria Arms glanced in our direction. His voice must have momentarily broken the background monotony of the music on the juke box. His accent set him apart, although in Oxford his accent wasn't as unusual as it might have been in Macclesfield.

'What are you studying then? At Brasenose,' I said, breaking a strange silence. Duncan seemed to have gone off into his own world.

'Oh, history. Not that it'll be of any use when I've finished.'

'So have you nearly finished or what?'

'I'm in my final year,' said Duncan. 'Finals in the summer. I haven't done a thing. Total, total disaster. My father's furious.'

All these things made it clear what his background was. I called my father Dad, he called his father Father. He probably called him that to his face. He would have breakfast, lunch and dinner. I had breakfast, dinner and tea.

'What does your father do?' I said, attempting to blend in as best I could.

'Daddy?' he said, confounding my theory. 'City.'

'City what?' I asked.

'City. As in, works in the.'

'What city?'

'The City. London. Stock Exchange. God, do you really not know what the City is?'

'Well, sort of. Yeah, I went there with my school, years ago. It was totally boring,' I said.

'Where did you go?'

'The Stock Exchange.'

'No. Which school?'

'Oh, right. Henry Box.'

'Can't say I've heard of it.'

'It's in Witney, about fourteen miles away.'

'Oh, Witney. Where the blankets come from.'

'Yep. What about you?' I asked.

'Eton,' said Duncan. 'Then a crammer in Kensington.'

'What? You went to Eton School?' I asked.

'Yah,' said Duncan.

'Bloody hell! I've never met anyone who's been to Eton before. What was it like?'

'Bloody awful,' said Duncan.

'D'you have to be clever to get in though?'

'What? To Eton? Are you kidding? Most of the chaps there are so unbelievably thick it's embarrassing. I mean seriously, seriously dense.'

'God, really, Eton!' I wanted to punch his lights out almost as much as I wanted to be him. To be able to drop a piece of information like that so easily set Duncan apart from the dull grey crowds that I was desperate to differentiate myself from. I'd seen pictures of these kids walking along the street. They still wore stand-up collars and little coats like Victorian school kids. They looked like prats and then grew up and ruled the country. They should all be put against a wall and shot. They were so confident and here was one talking to me, looking at me, smiling at me. I knew someone who went to Eton. I could tell people that. 'One of my friends went to Eton.' I could hear myself saying it. I was so impressed and yet I really believed they should all be machine-gunned, like in *If . . .*, which I hated because I knew it was made by public school boys who ruled the world.

'That's amazing!' I said.

'I say, Robbie,' said Duncan softly. 'Can I call you Robbie?'

'Yeah, if you want.'

'Well, you see, Robbie, I've been writing these children's stories. Well, they're not really for children, they're sort of fantasy stories, set in another time. In another reality. Call it a parallel universe, if you will.'

'Fantastic,' I said, not sure what he was on about.

'There's a chap I was at school with – used to fag for him – he runs this publishing company in London and he's really rather keen. It's sort of Tolkien meets Lewis, but far, far more, sort of, well, realistically, sort of, different. But I'd really like to find someone to illustrate them, sort of like Aubrey Beardsley, you know, and you draw cocks so well. D'you think you'd be interested?'

'Oh, far out,' I said, flattered almost speechless. 'Yeah, I'd love to do something like that. I've done loads and loads of drawings of like, well, yeah, and, yeah.' I had so much information to impart I could hardly speak. Duncan was the first person I'd met since leaving home who actually seemed to want to know what I thought.'

'There was this character I used to draw,' I said, 'called Captain Superbutch. It was a whole sort of jokey turn around on the super hero thing, you know, Superman, and Spiderman and all that crap. I nearly got it published by *International Times*. You know, Captain Superbutch was like a super hero, only his dick bulge is massive.'

'Dick bulge!' said Duncan. 'Goodness.'

'Yeah, really stupidly huge, and he went around flying on a sort of space chopper that looked like a giant breast.'

'Breast, like a, a breast, a woman's breast?'

'Yeah, a sort of space motor bike, a breast–bike sort of thing. With ape-hanger handlebars. It was just that he was a sort of joke on the men who are obsessed with tits.'

'Aren't you?'

'No,' I said remembering the aching erections I had experienced looking at pictures of same. But I was hooked into Captain Superbutch, I wasn't going to be swayed. 'Captain Superbutch tried to stop violence by killing loads and loads of people with his cock gun, a machine gun shaped like an erection, it was all a sort of send up.'

'Satire,' said Duncan.

'Yeah, that too,' I said happily.

'I bet it was fantastic,' said Duncan with a smile that made me feel rich. 'However, Robbie, it doesn't sound quite what I had in mind, but I'm sure it was very good.'

'Yeah, I did a whole mural on a wall.' It was in my bedroom at the parental home. 'In a commune I lived in, ages ago.'

'I was thinking more along the lines of witches and goblins,' said Duncan. 'And fairy kings. Mythical creatures ignored in the modern age.'

'Far out,' I said. 'Solid. Yeah, I'll do you some drawings.'

Duncan stood up and said, 'Have you got time for a snifter back at the college?'

'Babysitting.' I declined. 'Sorry. You see I promised Gary and Helen . . .'

He cut short my explanation by handing me a small folded sheaf of foolscap paper, scrawled all over in blue ink covered with dozens of corrections.

'This is just a rough,' he said. 'First draft stuff.'

That meant nothing to me. 'What is it?' I asked, looking at the crumpled paper.

'A manuscript, for the book I want you to illustrate.'

'Oh, right. The words.'

'Yes, Robbie, the words,' he said, tousling my hair as he held the door of the Victoria Arms open for me. I stepped out into the bitter night air. Our breath hung in clouds in front of our faces. A light blue Vauxhall Viva droned past, its square headlights grey and murky in the damp soup of mid-winter Oxford.

Duncan unlocked a woman's push bike with a basket on the front. 'I'll see you around soon, I hope,' he said and leaned near my face. I pulled back automatically, assuming he was drunk and had lost his balance. He smiled and pedalled off into the murk.

'He's a shirt lifter,' said Terry the next morning after I had told him about Duncan's appearance at the pub. 'He's one of those pouf society poufs. Don't tell me he shagged you?'

'No,' I said laughing. 'Anyway, what society is that?'

'I don't know. There's loads of them. Gay socs they're called. They all dress up like dead old poufs, the best sort,' said Terry, clattering silver teapots as if they were tools in a garage. 'They've got some society where they all wear long scarves and shag each other. Rubbing their great pouffy bodies together and spunking up in unison.'

This was at seven o'clock in the morning; there was never a time, it seemed, when Terry wasn't incensed by the level of homosexual activity going on around him. 'They're all poufs here,' he said.

'Even the women?' I asked.

'Lezzies,' he bawled. 'Muff munchers the lot of 'em. The women need a good shaggin' and the men should be lined up against a wall and shot up the arsehole. That'd stop 'em.'

There always came a time when I could stomach no more of Terry's bile and I retreated to the washing-up galley and made a start on all the leftovers from the night before.

Mr Willis appeared at the door. 'We need you tonight, Robert,' he said. 'Pilson's fallen ill and we've got the Honorary Doctors and three Emeritus Professors coming up for the evening. Can you serve at High Table?'

'I don't know,' I said. 'I've helped people at buffet evenings when my mum's done a smorgasbord type meal.'

Mr Willis rubbed his eyes hard, grimaced and looked at me as he chewed his lip. 'Well, we're a bit short, so it would help if you could fetch and carry this evening. You'll get a bit of overtime.'

'Brilliant,' I said.

'Watch it when you're bending over serving the veg,' said Terry. We ate in the kitchen, sitting around a big table after the main lunch had been served and cleaned up. 'They'll finger you as you try and do a silver service.'

'Terry, please,' said Mr Willis. 'Ladies present.'

'Sorry, Mr Willis,' said Terry rapidly, keeping his head down. He really was a sad case when I came to think about it. As people started to clear away their things he mumbled to me, 'Watch them though, especially the old fuckers. They're all raving poufs.'

After lunch I had to practise serving vegetables from a silver tray. I had to learn to hold a fork and spoon in one hand as if they were chopsticks and use them to serve carrots. I was hopeless. I dropped them again and again. Poor old Mr Willis remained admirably calm throughout the afternoon, until slowly we came to a compromise where I could hold the fork and spoon together and scoop the carrots up. I was to say, 'Carrots, sir?' to each person at High Table, although I still had no clear idea what High Table was. I imagined a big room with a lot of low tables, and one high one where all the old dons and professors sat.

All afternoon I was sent to do dozens of errands for the chef, who never actually spoke directly to me. I had to buy seven pounds of onions in the covered market, on account, so I didn't have to take money. I had to help three other members of staff carry the heavy silver plates and jugs from the top store room.

When I eventually saw the inside of the old dining room, I couldn't believe the wealth and medieval splendour it contained. I'd walked past the outside many times, never really bothering to look up at the ceiling, although it is visible from the quad, a high old hammer-beam roof structure like in Westminster Great Hall. I'd done a project on this style of roof structure at school. I had even made one beam construction out of balsa wood, which Vincent Pickering had broken.

Below the roof, on the walls, loads of tapestries and name plates were hung, and pictures and thick curtains; richness, everywhere there was richness. All the tables were highly polished dark wood, really medieval looking, beautifully kept. The whole place was immaculate; it smelt wonderful and rich: of furniture polish, flowers, the scent of long-term, in-built, powerful success.

The diners entered the hall without my knowledge. I followed Terry up the corridor to the back entrance and overheard a Latin prayer being said. I pulled my hair back and tied it tightly with an elastic band, which, as anyone with long hair will tell you, can be very painful.

'That's fuckin' red rag to a bull, mate,' said Terry, flicking my pony-tail. 'They just want to bite that with their teeth as they bury the old pork, mate.' He grimaced and mimed a thrusting desperation. I started to giggle. This was cut short by a bustle of hushed activity around me.

'Ready, Robert,' said Mr Willis, giving me a final inspection, pulling my collar down. None of the clothes I was wearing really fitted me, but it was too late to do anything about that.

We had to run the food up from the kitchens in a panic once the hall was full, and it was packed. I recognized quite a few of the posh old blokes at High Table from the television, from political interview programmes, though I didn't know their names. I didn't care because to me they were all fascists anyway. Anyone in a suit with that special 'Ahh, I'm so comfortable' smile was a fascist as far as I was concerned.

They had soup first; there didn't seem a lot of choice there. I didn't serve any of that, I just poured soup into bowls with a ladle. 'Faster please, Robert, we have 400 people here and I don't want any of them waiting,' said Mr Willis.

I went around collecting bowls almost immediately, and as soon as I'd passed a huge pile of empty bowls to Terry, who threw them on a tray in the corridor out the back, I was handed my carrots. They were piled up, sliced and buttered, on a large silver dish. I walked along behind these wealthy, successful men who smelt of aftershave and recent bathing, saying, 'Carrots, sir?'

Then I walked behind the remaining diners, all just older than me, all dressed up in white shirts, dark suits and bow ties. All were very intent on their conversations. Some of them were talking about sex, some of them were talking about writers, some of them were even talking in Latin. Four hundred times I said, 'Carrots, sir?' They all wanted them. I don't think there was one person there who said, 'Not for me, thanks.' I placed the carrots with my spoon and fork, hooked together and gripped in a panic, on their plates, already piled up with a rich meaty dish. I had to return to the serving area to pick up three new silver trays of carrots. Once I'd served the last plate, I walked quickly back to the serving area.

'Okay, now, get ready to clear the plates,' said Mr Willis in hushed tones.

'But we've only just doled it all out!' I said, looking for somewhere to sit down. There was nowhere.

'The dons have nearly finished,' said Mr Willis, who was motioning to some of the other staff to get ready. Within moments we were charging through the crowds picking up plates and piling them to ludicrous heights on a side table. Terry was humping these piles on to his trolley, out of sight. I put my head through the door at one moment, to see what he was up to.

'Been fingered yet?' he asked.

'No, they've obviously all shagged each other before they came to dinner,' I joked.

'Oh, yeah,' said Terry, completely seriously. 'They're all pulling each other off under the table.' He then mimed someone sitting at a table eating and having an orgasm. He mimed the person sitting next to the orgasmee furiously masturbating him with a grimace. I fell on the floor laughing. It was the funniest thing I had ever seen.

'Robert. Please,' said Mr Willis, who was standing right behind me. 'Control yourself. The diners can hear you. What's going on, Terry?'

'I don't know, Mr Willis, sir. He just started laughing.'

'Well, we've all got far too much to do to stand around laughing, haven't we, Terry?'

'That's right, Mr Willis, sir,' said Terry, who crashed another pile of plates on to his heavily laden tray.

'It's time to serve the sweet,' said Mr Willis.

'Bloody hell!' I said. 'Haven't they had enough?'

They had jam roly-poly for pudding. Not some fancy French fruit tart, or profiteroles, or just fruit, but jam roly-poly. I was serving custard, pouring it from a huge, very heavy silver jug.

'Custard, sir?' They all wanted custard. There wasn't one person out of the 400 who didn't want custard.

I flopped down in the corner of the washing-up galley when we had finally finished clearing up all the mess. There must have been at least twenty people involved in feeding the High Table, all rushing around like mad, trying not to make any noise.

I got home at about 11.30, threw Cabbage some left-over meat I'd brought back in a plastic bag and went straight to bed.

Two days later I was back in the damn kitchen. I was thinking about the illustrations to Duncan's book, wanting to capture some of the magic of the interiors of the old college. I imagined he'd like that. I wanted to draw with my Rotring pen, and then colour in with those special opaque inks, all rich and carefully done. I wanted to depict rich cloths hanging from stone walls in old mountain-top castles. Strange creatures, half man, half beast, wearing cloaks and green tights with big, floppy leather boots. This was it, the break I'd been waiting for. I could see myself living in a sun-drenched medieval cottage somewhere exotic, like Herefordshire, sitting in a big studio doing drawings for Duncan's books. There would be women there, outside my window, women in long dresses who wore wellington boots and had strong brown arms. I'd watch them pitching hay into a barn and then one would turn and smile at me, her white teeth contrasting with her pretty brown face, and she would beckon me to go to her . . .

'I found that copy of *Carfax Comic*,' said Duncan, his head suddenly appearing around the door of the kitchen. 'The one with your drawings in. I loved it, you draw cocks very well,' he said with a big grin.

'Thanks,' I said, not really knowing how to take his compliment. I almost started saying that my cock-drawing abilities were greatly enhanced by my early exposure to the school of Tom of Finland, but I managed to shut myself up. It hadn't been hard to work out that Duncan wanted to have some form of sexual contact with me. I wasn't sure what he wanted to do but I was pretty sure I didn't want to do it back. However, in my loneliness, I found his attention very flattering.

'Please don't delay my staff for too long, sir,' said Mr Willis as he passed. He smiled at me flatly which made me feel even less comfortable. Duncan sneered at Mr Willis's back and turned his attention to me again.

'So, tell me, Robbie. You don't live with your parents then?'

'No, no. I moved away from home years ago. I'm an urban peasant.'

'Are you?' said Duncan. 'How marvellous. What d'you do to become one of those?'

'I don't know,' I said, thrown off my normal course by yet another strange question. 'You just become one. The people I live with, well, all the houses opposite the Viccy Arms, well, more or less all of them, they're sort of like a commune, only an urban one, and they sort of live differently. They live a basic, sort of totally urban peasant sort of existence.'

'Sounds brilliant,' said Duncan. He looked behind himself to see if anyone was in the corridor. Considering what happened next it must have been all clear.

He walked up to me and embraced me and said, 'You are so beautiful, Robbie.'

'D'you want some tea?' I asked. The question appeared in my mouth and made me feel young and stupid, two things I hated feeling. This was as uncomfortable a moment as I had ever known. Plus I was resisting an unbelievable urge to scratch my nose.

'No, I want to kiss you. Can I?' said Duncan, his face too close for me to read.

I felt my nose crease up, which partially relieved the itch. I shrugged. He gently kissed me on the lips and slowly worked away until his tongue was rollicking around in my mouth. I felt totally unmoved by his efforts. His breath tasted stale, of tobacco and weird garlicky, rancid stuff, very pungent and not in the least erotic. I mentally checked to see if I was having anything resembling an erection as there was no obvious sensation. I wasn't. Duncan broke off the kiss.

'Oh, God. You're the most beautiful boy I've ever seen,' he said breathily and too close.

'Thanks,' I said, not knowing how to deal with such a compliment.

'No, I really mean it. I couldn't believe it that first day I saw you. I've been able to think of nothing else.'

'Yeah, well, look. I don't know,' I said, looking for a term to use which would get me out of this.

'I'm sorry,' said Duncan, backing off and running his hands through his hair. 'I'm sorry, I've been too forward. I'm so sorry, but you drive me crazy. I can't sleep at night because I'm thinking about you. I'm behind in my studies, I'm losing control, Robbie. Please help me.'

I didn't know what to do. This man had been thinking about me so much he couldn't sleep. A posh student who'd been to Eton, who wore straight clothes and had a strange thin-lipped smile, fancied me, Rob the cartoonist. It didn't really make sense.

'Come to my rooms this afternoon,' said Duncan. 'Please.'

'I've got to get back to feed my dog.'

'Dog!' said Duncan.

'Yeah, she's called Cabbage. She's a lurcher pup, very well behaved though.'

'Oh, God!' said Duncan biting his thumb. 'You drive me crazy and you've got to go and feed your dog called Cabbage. This is so rich, Robbie. Fabulously rich. Listen, please.' His hands were gripped in white knuckle pleading. 'Please come up. I'm in D7. D staircase in the main quad. Please come up and we can have tea and discuss our plans for the book.'

'Oh yeah,' I said, suddenly remembering the roll of paper.

'What did you think of the manuscript, by the way?'

'I haven't read it yet,' I said. 'I will though, I had too much to do last night.' I was lying, in fact I couldn't even remember where I had left the manuscript.

Mr Willis appeared behind Duncan without any

warning. Gently he put a patronizing hand on Duncan's shoulder, not a popular move with the old Etonian.

'Please, sir, my staff are hard enough to control as it is.' Mr Willis laughed, a thing I'd never seen him do before. He turned to me and said with a peculiarly jolly tone to his voice, 'There's toast to be made please, Robert.'

'Yeah, okay. Sorry,' I said, for once grateful that I had been ordered to do something. Duncan stalked off, taking long strides down the stone corridor. His black leather shoes had steel tips sunk into the heels which made them click loudly. I went into the kitchen and started making the toast, with Mr Willis right behind me.

'It seems to be for the best in the long run, Robert,' he said carefully, judging his words and making much of looking out of the window, 'if you don't fraternize with the students too much.' He smiled, his lips sealed. 'Best for all parties.'

'Yeah, well, he came to see me,' I said defensively. Mr Willis nodded.

'I know, I know,' he said, 'but maybe if you cut your hair and didn't wear such flamboyant clothes, you'd have a few less visits.' He nodded some more. It was almost camp, the way he pursed his lips and looked at my skin-tight, patched, flared jeans.

Mr Willis spun on his heel and walked out of the kitchen, busy now with breakfast preparation. I threw in a few slices of bread and looked for Terry's copy of the *Sun*. It wasn't in its normal place.

As I turned back to the toaster a large black and white picture of a naked woman was held up right in front of my face. The woman was young and dark, her belly taut from holding it in for the photographer; her breasts were large and fascinating, her face soft, welcoming, desperately sexually arousing. I stared at the picture, absorbing every detail.

'I would shag her into next week,' said Terry, shattering my soft romantic dreams of sexual love. 'She'd be beggin' for more, and I'd give it her. I'd shag that to death, mate. Look at the tits on it! Fuckin' hell!'

Terry walked off, giving a large cooking pot stored under a prep table a hearty kick of disgust. This absurd act of aggression from Terry, which would normally have made me laugh or feel slightly sorry for him, made me angry. I couldn't fathom out where the feeling came from.

The pressure I felt from Duncan was unexpected and disturbing. I had a little routine working at the college which made me feel safe. I had even paid some money – about £15 – into my building society. Everything seemed to be sorted out, tidy, safe. Until that morning.

Mr Willis may have seen me being kissed by Duncan, or worse still, Terry may have seen it or would hear about it and I would be on the receiving end of his shirt-lifting, turd-burgling barbs.

As I stared at the beautiful page three girl in the *Sun*, I thought how, if Duncan had been a woman, that kiss would have been so romantic. My flirtation with homosexuality must have ended there, above the toaster in the kitchens of Brasenose College, Oxford. Till then I'd taken quite an interest in the subject, perhaps for intellectual and fashion-based reasons. The GLF, the Gay Lib Front, (everything was a Front in those days), was very trendy and very attractive to me. I had read an article in *Rolling Stone* called 'Suck Cock, Beat The Draft' about homosexual draft dodgers in America. They were really hip and revolutionary, I thought. I had worn a Gay Lib badge for a whole day the previous summer which had a powerful effect on everyone who saw it. Some men shoved me hard in the chest as I passed them in the streets, some women teased me, two builders loading a van grabbed their crotches as I passed and shouted, 'Ben Doon and Phil McAverty', for some reason. I don't know if they were introducing themselves or referring to me.

David Bowie had worn a long blue dress when I saw him play at the Oxford Apollo. And I had sat in a trendy London apartment and listened to Lou Reed's album *Transformer*, with the song 'Walk on the Wild Side' playing loud on the big Bang & Olufsen stereo.

> Shaved his legs and then he was a she,
> She said, Hey Babe, take a walk on the wild side.

I had painted my nails and walked languorously, I wanted to be so attractive, so naughty and sexy. The imagery, the way I could see myself dragged up, eye-linered and lip-glossed was so different from the image I got of myself when I pored over a copy of *Men Only* or *Escort*. I didn't fit into the world of Penthouse Pet executive pornography. The previous summer I'd walked through Allie's parents' back garden in a yellow dress, a bright yellow dress which Allie had worn to a party in Indooroopilly, in Australia, the previous year. I didn't dare venture into the streets of Witney wearing it, but it felt great, it felt *revolutionary*. Allie and I had discussed the fascism of men's clothes as I sat sipping orange juice and smoking a joint. Allie had her feet dipping in the filthy disused swimming pool, which lay overgrown and hidden at the bottom of their enormous garden. She was wearing nothing except a pair of knickers. It was a wonderful afternoon. Me in a dress, talking to a nearly naked girl. We didn't have sex, although poor Allie may have been trying.

And yet however much this might seem to point to an unfocused homosexual drive, when I was with a man who actually wanted to have sex with me my penis shrank, and when I was alone, looking at a woman's naked body in the *Sun* newspaper, I was as erect as it was possible to be.

That was the dichotomy: I was a gay heterosexual. There was a sort of joke going around at the time that said some men posed as being gay because they knew they would get off with more women, women being sick of macho men. If this is so, it never happened to me. I only ever experienced sexual approaches from other men.

The toaster started belching smoke. I hated making toast, I hated being forced to spend so much of my time in the kitchens. I wanted to roam across wild moorland. I wanted to go back to Llanbedr and wake up to the crisp morning air, smoke a roll-up and build a geodesic dome. I wanted to have sex with a smooth brown woman with breasts. I didn't want to snog with a garlic-breathed student, even if it was in an oak-panelled fifteenth-century room in Brasenose College.

I felt an immense wave of relief when I left work that day. I unlocked my bike and rode along the cobbled lane at the side of Brasenose as fast as I could, the loose mud guard over my back wheel rattling in true Oxford tradition. I got back to St Bernards Road in a couple of minutes and found Cabbage out in the back garden; she was thrilled to see me and washed my face with her warm tongue. Then I made some tea for Helen who was sitting playing with Daisy, and I felt safe again. 'I'm going to leave Brasenose,' I said.

'But you've only just started!' said the bursar when I went in a week later to tell him I was leaving. I'd had to make an appointment and the week's wait had made me more determined rather than less.

'I know, but I get depressed,' I said. 'I feel trapped.'

'We all get depressed, Robert, we all feel trapped. That's what life's about,' he said, laughing through closed teeth. He looked a bit like an older John Cleese. The mouth and the eyes never matched, the smile was never to be believed because the eyes were so clearly depressed.

'Yeah, well I want to start up my own university,' I said, 'in Wales, in a geodesic dome.'

'Your own university!' said the bursar, seemingly genuine in his surprise. 'And what would you teach there, Robert?'

'Well, that's the whole point, no one would teach because that's fascist. You'd go there to learn from one another, in a playful sort of way.'

'Playful,' said the bursar.

'Yeah, instead of all this heavy stuff you do here. All the students are so depressed, they're always killing themselves.' There had been a story in the *Oxford Mail* the previous week of how a student from Corpus Christi had hanged himself in a bedsit off the Cowley Road.

'Oh, I hardly . . .'

'Anyway, I can't take it any more. I'm dropping out. I've realized that I didn't make all the effort to drop out just to get a job in a kitchen. It was a mistake that I came to work here in the first place.'

'It seems such a shame, though. You do your job well. Mr Willis is pleased with your progress.'

The bursar pleaded with me a little longer, then lost interest. As I left his office, feeling powerful and pleased with myself, I saw Terry pushing a trolley full of coffee things on the other side of the quad. It reassured me in my conviction that I had to leave, no matter what. I didn't want to end up like Terry, seething with bile and hatred for the people I had to serve and be polite to.

'Wotcher, wanker,' he said when I met up with him. 'Just been serving coffee to a bunch of Jap cunts in the SCR. Over here to give the college more money. Wonder if I'll get a pay rise.'

'No chance,' I said glumly.

'Yeah, the tight bastards, keep all the money for theirselves, living it up like kings. I'd like to bomb the lot of them. Get some of them RIA mates of yours to do it.'

'It's IRA, and they're not my mates.'

'All right, brain box. So why aren't you a student then, if you're so fuckin' clever?'

'I'm going to be. But I'm going to set up my own university, in Wales.'

'Oh, yeah. Brilliant idea. When's that then, the twelfth of never?'

'No, really, really soon. I'm leaving here. I've just handed my notice in to the bursar.'

'Fuckin' hell. You idiot. This is a cushy job, what you want to go and do a thing like that for?'

'I can't take it, I feel trapped, selling my time for a pittance.'

'You fuckin' idiot. It's good money here,' said Terry. 'You don't know what it's like out there.' He gestured towards the entrance gate as we walked past. 'It's rough. There's no free food, you get paid rotten money, there's no security. Listen, I was always being made redundant before I came here. You don't know what it's like being poor, do you?'

'Yes, I do. I was really broke before I came here. I didn't have a penny.'

'Yeah, but if you were starving, you could have gone back to Mummy and Daddy any time. I'm talking poor where you haven't got anyone to turn to, mate. What you going to do when you leave here?'

'Drop out,' I said. 'I've done it before. Only this time I've saved up some money to start up my university.'

'How much?'

'Twenty-seven pounds.'

'You're fuckin' mad, mate,' said Terry, ramming the trolley through the entrance door to the kitchens. 'I reckon you been listening to those pouffy snobs from the Piers wassisname club. They just want to shag you up the arse, mate. You fall for that, you deserve to be shagged.'

'That's why I want to leave,' I said, my voice high pitched and embarrassing. 'I'm sick of the snobby people here, and their fascist attitudes. I want to bomb this place too. It makes me sick. They're so privileged and they take it all for granted, and the ones that don't, kill themselves. I'm sick of it.'

On my last day working at Brasenose College, as I was doing the toast, I turned around and saw the woman I had met on New Year's Eve standing in the breakfast queue, talking animatedly. My mind started to race. This was meant to be, the last morning at work and she appears! She would ask me out and I'd be able to go, we'd go back to her rooms in Worcester College, and we'd snog and I'd want to, and we'd definitely have sex and she'd take me to strange distant lands and introduce me to rich, famous people. I was really excited when I handed her a plate of buttered toast and said, 'Hello, there.'

She looked at me quizzically for a moment, then allowed herself a small smile.

'It's me, Robert. I met you in Builth Wells, on New Year's Eve.'

She raised her head, nodded very slowly and then said, 'Oh, yes.' She smiled, took the toast and continued to talk to her friend.

I turned away to hide my hurt from her. I didn't want

her to know. I felt so completely useless, insignificant, pointless and wasted. I didn't even feel angry, I just wanted to be away from there, for ever. I bit my lip and shook my head over the toaster. 'Never again, never again will I work for you fucking horrible people,' I said to myself, making sure all the toast was slightly scorched.

8

Boom Shanka

Boom Shanka. The words were painted on the lid of Charlie's wooden chest in weird, Eastern-type script. Charlie was making a sandwich with white sliced bread, big chunks of butter and honey. White sliced bread was something I had never eaten. I'd been brought up to eat brown bread, and since I'd left home I only ever ate heavy, organic home-made sort of bread.

'What's "Boom Shanka"?' I asked.

'It's what Afghanistan farmers shout when they toke up huge amounts of dope in massive chillums,' said Charlie. He mimed smoking a chillum, and shouted, 'Boom Shanka!' as he exhaled a cloud of imaginary smoke, his fingers drawing the smoke curls rising above his head.

'Yeah, man,' I said laughing. I repeated the mime. 'Boom Shanka.'

'Acid logic,' said Charlie as his bad teeth tore into his soft bread sandwich. His wooden chest was where he kept everything he owned: bread, butter, knife, cat food for a little grey kitten called Chillum, long black cloak and brown leather boots with stars painted on them.

He had a small mattress on the floor and some weird, impossible-to-decipher posters on the walls. His room smelt of patchouli oil, incense and dope. He had really long hair, flared white jeans with patches and wore a shirt of thin blue material, cut much too big and loose. He represented everything the urban peasants thought was daft and frivolous; stupid old half-baked hippie philosophy poured from Charlie in torrents. He'd read every stupid hippie book ever published, could quote from them at random and yet seemed utterly unaffected by what they had to say.

'Chillum, what you need is a little nourishment,' said Charlie as he used the same knife he'd spread his butter and honey with to dole out some pungent-smelling, fish-based cat food.

Charlie was the man I'd seen on Magdalene Bridge when I was going to the interview at Brasenose. I met him standing outside his house on St Bernards Road the day I came back from the college with my last pay cheque. It all seemed psychic and Jungian, synchronistic even, though I wasn't sure what that meant. It felt like I was meant to go through the experience of working at the college and earn a bit of money to see that it wasn't worth it, that selling your time to someone was really selling your whole life, and they would never pay enough. I had £27 in the bank and felt quite rich but now I knew I had to continue on my journey.

'Hi, man. What's happening, like? Are you hanging out or what?' he asked, his voice a mixture of public school English and nasal West Coast American.

'Yeah, well, sort of,' I said. 'Just jacked in my job. Thinking of hitting the road.'

'Jack Kerouac, man,' said Charlie, for no clear reason.

I thought it best to agree. I chose a hippie book I'd read the previous year. '*Electric KoolAid Acid Test*,' I said.

'Yeah. Right,' said Charlie, looking up and down the street like a nervous pimp. 'Hey, we're having a party tonight. You should come. There'll be some good blow, some cool people. It'll be really hip, man.'

'Brilliant,' I said. 'What time?'

'Time is relative, man,' said Charlie, this time sounding like Keith Richards from the Rolling Stones. 'Just come when your karma pulls you this way.'

'Heavy,' I said.

I spent most of the day in bed, reading and sleeping, and that evening I sat with Gary and Helen, feeling like their son. We had a meal together in silence. They were rowing a lot and Daisy was crying; it wasn't the happiest house to be in.

'I'm going to a party,' I said as I washed up the new metal bowls Gary had bought.

'I thought you were going to babysit,' said Gary.

'Oh, sorry. I didn't know,' I said, looking at Helen.

'Did you ask Robert?' she enquired.

'No, he always babysits.'

'I always ask first,' said Helen, knitting and not looking up, reminding me of Dandy Nichols in *Till Death Us Do Part*.

'I was busy. I was out working with Roger, trying to earn a crust.'

'I'm going out,' said Helen. 'It's my turn, you can do what you like, as long as there's someone here with Daisy.'

'I'll have to stay in, then,' said Gary, looking at me.

'Well, I haven't been out much,' I said defensively. 'I've been invited to a party down the road, at number 49.'

'What, the hippie house?' said Gary with a sneer.

'They're young people, having fun, not that you'd remember,' said Helen.

'They're bloody hippies, woman,' snapped Gary. 'Wrapped up in all that crap. I saw one of them wearing a cloak this morning.'

'That's Charlie. He's from America,' I said.

'He's a wanker,' said Gary. 'He had a fucking cloak on, with a cat sitting on his shoulder.'

'That's Chillum,' I said. Gary sneered again, shook his head and started rolling a cigarette. How could someone who'd so recently had hair longer than any of us now be as intolerant as a middle-class bank operative, sneering at people who weren't like him? It made me depressed. I was disappointed, which meant only one thing. I had to move on. I had attached myself to this group, and as I got to know them I realized they were not quite as special as I had hoped. Their spiritual quest, which had at one time seemed like the way politically and spiritually, had been left next to the ashtray in the Viccy Arms one night and no one noticed.

I left Gary reading the local free paper, the only reading material in the house except for Duncan's manuscript, which was rolled up and stuffed inside my broken-down snakeskin boots, thrown in the corner of my barren little bedroom.

When I got to the door of number 49, all of thirty yards from my house, there was almost a queue of young people outside. They all had long hair, parted in the middle, and they all had thick greatcoats and big boots on. They all smelled of patchouli oil; they had bracelets on their wrists and beads around their necks; and some of the women had headbands around their heads. They were all smoking cigarettes like it was going out of style, which it wasn't. I entered the crowded hall and saw Charlie standing at the foot of the stairs, his cloak still on, but no kitten.

'Hey man, welcome to vice city. Let us commence the stoning of our brains.'

'Yeah, brilliant,' I said and followed him slowly upstairs, past throngs of talking teenagers. I hadn't seen so many people the same age as me since I'd left school. Everywhere I looked there were very attractive young women with long hair who smoked and pretty certainly had sex. They were talking to young men who had long

hair but looked clean and well scrubbed. I knew somehow that they were all still at school, studying for their A
levels.

I entered Charlie's room and saw his wooden chest.
Boom Shanka.

'Cool party,' I said as I exhaled a thick cloud of real
dope smoke and passed the well-made joint back to
Charlie. Something about the way the papers were stuck
together reminded me of a model aeroplane with a
balsa-wood frame covered with thin tissue paper.

'Some of the people here are really weird,' said Charlie
with a pinch-faced sneer. A man with very long hair
walked into the room. He wore it parted neatly in the
middle and it hung down in a thin sheet either side of his
sharp-featured face.

'This is Gollum. He's really weird,' said Charlie.

'Evening, Charlie boy,' said Gollum with a slight burr
of Oxfordshire accent.

'We're at the same school, man,' said Charlie. I was
surprised but said nothing. Somehow Charlie's look and
living situation didn't immediately make you think
schoolboy.

'Where's that?' I asked.

'Magdalene,' said Gollum.

'What, the college?'

'No man, the school, over Magdalene Bridge.'

'I saw you there, with Chillum on your shoulder, ages
ago.'

'Yeah man,' said Gollum. 'That's when Charlie brought
his cat to school. They freaked out.'

'Yeah, had to go back home. They're really heavy in
Mordor,' said Charlie. The reference evaded me. Charlie
noticed. 'Mordor, man. The centre of the evil empire,
Ashk Naz Gimbataluk. *Lord of the Rings*, man.'

I had yet to read the Tolkien classic. Had I done so it would have explained a lot about Duncan and his peculiar fantasy world. I nodded and accepted the joint again as it did the circuit.

'Boom Shanka,' said a new arrival with a mop of thick, dirty-looking curls. He was wearing ripped dark velvet loon pants, yellow painted boots and a well-worn fur coat, cut off as a short jacket.

'Hey, Mark, man. Far out!' said Charlie, offering Mark the joint. A woman appeared out of the darkness behind him. Her face half obscured by hair, she was wrapped up in another cut-off fur coat, faded flared jeans and clogs. She sat cross-legged on the floor near Charlie and smoked a cigarette.

I was completely stoned by this time, but feeling very relaxed. We smoked dope like soldiers smoke cigarettes: there were always three or four joints going around, and someone was always making a new one. There was music coming from somewhere in the house, muffled and threatening, a background craziness. Charlie's room was in a thick fug of vibes. Charlie had noticed too.

'Intense vibes,' he said as he started to spread peanut butter on a thin slice of Mother's Pride. 'And I've got the munchies, man!'

'Yeah,' said Mark with the thick mop of hair. I looked at the girl sitting in the corner, she didn't say anything.

Charlie delved into his Boom Shanka box and held up a yellow and pink cake covered in marzipan. 'It's Battenberg time!' he said, and laughed in the way that Gilbert Shelton's Furry Freak Brothers did when Fat Freddy raided a convenience store, driven insane by dope-induced Munchie Madness.

The Battenberg cake was passed around like a joint, each person sitting round the room taking a bite and passing it on. They munched and said words like 'fantastic' and 'incredible'.

I was suddenly shaken by a vicious thirst: a special doper's thirst, a mind-boggling need, a thick, stringy and hard-to-shift thirst which had to be dealt with. Smoking dope always made me thirsty. I got up and went downstairs, past thick throngs of people, everyone smoking and talking. There was loud music playing. It might have been Captain Beefheart or some disturbing section from a Frank Zappa album. I looked into the gloom. From what I could see, no one was dancing, only talking. I went out to where the kitchens should have been, but in this house it was just a black hole smelling of cats and damp. I turned around and went through the house, out of the front door and over to the Victoria Arms, where I ordered a double orange juice. The pub was very busy, my ears were making a constant rushing sound and my stomach muscles were stretched taut. Phrases and words kept repeating themselves in my head.

As I sank the orange juice in one hit I noticed the blue lights flashing in the upside-down whisky bottle hanging behind the bar. I turned to see the entire clientele of the Victoria Arms looking out of the window at the police raid taking place at number 49. Without any register of fear, I left the pub and went to see what was happening. There seemed to be hundreds of police milling about; four or five police cars and vans had pulled up on the pavement. No one was running away in a panic; everyone seemed to be standing around quietly in the bitter night air. I saw the girl with the fur coat walk across the end of the street with Mark, the crazy mopped-hair man. I surmised they must have fled from the back of the house and were creeping off into the night. I liked the way the girl walked: big strides, long slim legs, her round velvet-covered bum just showing below her fur jacket. Her clogs clopped along Walton Street with that special clog sound that carries over the sound of traffic.

Charlie was escorted from the house in handcuffs. He was smiling. As he passed me he said, 'Battenberg,' through a mouthful of cake. I laughed, then my arm was grabbed by a short stocky man in a leather jacket. My heart rate shot up as he firmly but gently guided me to the side of the front door of number 49.

'Let's see what you're carrying, shall we?' he said and started going through my pockets. I felt humiliated by the experience. Other young people standing around on the street looked on sympathetically but did nothing. Everyone was stoned and didn't really know what to do.

'Shoes off,' he said. I took my shoes off and stood on the freezing pavement in my stocking feet while he felt around their sweaty interior. He found nothing on me except a five pound note, some change, Cabbage's lead and a packet of twenty No. 6 cigarettes, with the flip top still intact.

'Okay, you're clean. Where d'you live?' he asked. I pointed up the road.

'D'your parents know you're out?'

'No,' I said. 'I don't live with them. I left home years ago. I live in a commune.'

'A commune. Where's that, then?' asked the policeman.

'Number 45.'

'You're a squatter?' he asked incredulously.

'Yeah,' I said proudly. I hadn't been called that before and it sounded good. My heart rate reduced to merely beating very fast as opposed to sounding like an outboard motor at full throttle. He asked my name, age, previous address, parents' address, the last school I attended, everything, writing it all down in a little book.

'I'm keeping my eye on you,' he said, and disappeared

into the night. I sighed deeply and lit up a cigarette. Gollum approached, his hands buried in the pockets of his greatcoat.

'Charlie's been arrested, man. Got a cigarette?' He held up two fingers in a smoking gesture, moving them back and forth to and from his mouth. He kept this movement up while I opened the packet and offered him one. He lit up and pocketed my matches. 'Bad scene, man. Bad scene. They found half an ounce in his box, man, ripped his room apart. They stormed the house like Nazis. Someone here's a grass. Where were you, man?' said Gollum, his face even weirder under street lights. 'I didn't see you when they came in. You're not an undercover pig, are you?' I felt guilty. Had I the benefit of experience I would have known that although the police use all manner of officers for undercover work, they rarely get the chance to employ a sixteen year old.

'I got searched out here,' I said defensively. 'The guy was really heavy, but I'm not carrying so he couldn't do anything. You could see he was furious, though. They've been trying to get me for months.'

This lie seemed to cheer Gollum. 'What for, man?'

'I know a load of people in the Angry Brigade,' I said, 'and I was really involved in, like, revolutionary stuff. Street theatre and demonstrations and stuff.'

'Wow, amazing,' said Gollum.

'So, like, a whole load of pigs are just desperate to bust me. That's why I've got to be careful.'

'Understood, Robbie, man. Understood,' said Gollum, his face momentarily lit by the red glow of his already stubby No. 6.

'But it's a total bummer for Charlie, though,' I said. The realization that Charlie was in a police station was only just dawning on me.

'Yeah, man. But his dad, like, runs Oxford.'

'Really? Oh, wow. Brilliant.'

'Yeah, he's, like, boss man of the whole university. The big professor. Charlie and his sister live up at Hilltop with him, man. He's cool.'

'I thought Charlie lived here.'

'Yeah, here, yeah, sure,' said Gollum. 'But, like, we all go and hang out up at Hilltop sometimes. If his stepmum is away, which she is at the moment. Come up sometime, man. It's fantastic.' Gollum sloped off into the night.

I went to bed that night feeling elated, Cabbage snuggled up next to me. I stroked her wiry hair and she made some excellent satisfied-dog grunting sounds as she settled down for the night.

I started to fantasize about Charlie's dad's house. I imagined his father as a tall, gaunt man with long grey hair tied in a pony-tail. I had a vision of this Hilltop place being some sort of castle outside Oxford, up a long winding drive bordered by rhododendrons. There would be hundreds of young people living there happily, in medieval clothes, sitting around being spiritual.

We'd sit around in the old castle dining hall, with huge log fires burning at either end and large dogs lying around. I'd wear green tights and have a brown leather boxy jacket on, with a belt and pouch for my tobacco and money hanging sexily from my waist. I'd sit near Charlie's sister, people would laugh at my stories, then she'd gently put her hand on mine and lead me up some stone steps, her long dress hanging loosely from her firm figure . . .

The dream ended in the normal way and I fell into a blissful sleep.

I awoke at midday the next day, with no one in the house. Gary was at work, Helen was out shopping, the washing-up was done and neatly stacked. I went outside and walked across the back gardens, since all the fences had long gone. The back door to Charlie's house was wide open. The small back room was littered with old curtains, cigarette ends, a battered stereo, album covers and a mattress with someone sleeping on it. It didn't look like Charlie, so I walked upstairs. Charlie was sitting on his box writing something in a small notebook. In the seconds that I caught a glimpse of it, I could see it had cartoon drawings as well as writing.

'Busted, man,' said Charlie, slamming the book shut and putting it on the chest. 'Quarter of an ounce of top grade Red Leb, man. It was good dope, wasn't it, man?'

'Fantastic,' I said. 'I was smashed out of my skull, got searched on the street and really hassled, but they couldn't find anything. They let you out, though.'

'Yeah, the old man got me out this morning. Told me they haven't got a case because of the warrant. The police say they were responding to a report of a riot.'

'A riot!' I said, feeling that I was part of it.

'Yeah, man. They call that a riot. Wow, I'd like to see their faces at a real riot, man.'

'Like a huge anti-Vietnam demo.'

'Ho, Ho, Ho Chi Minh.'

I joined in. 'Ho, Ho, Ho Chi Minh.' We chanted together, punching the air with our clenched fists. Then there was a silence, until Charlie picked up a torn paperback book and threw it into his wooden chest. The police had clearly been brutal with his possessions, which were scattered all over the room.

'So what have you got to do?' I asked.

'Bailed out, got to go back to the old man's place at Hilltop till the case comes up.'

Hilltop! This was my chance to go to the castle.

'D'you need a hand moving stuff? I could use the

door-mobile,' I said. Since business had started to grow for Gary and the urban peasants, they had invested in a clapped-out Bedford van which they were forever fixing in the back garden. The wonderful old door-mobile was standing idle at the back of Roger's house.

'Hey, yeah. Transcendental, man,' said Charlie.

The journey from St Bernards Road to the top of Headington Hill is not a huge one when compared to the long march to start the People's Republic of China, or Hannibal traversing the Alps on elephants. It's about three miles, with a steepish hill towards the end, but for two skinny, lanky adolescents who thought the desire for good health and strength was strongly linked to Nazi ideology, pushing an old oak door loaded up with wooden chests and mattresses, posters and Indian wall-hangings was hovering on the very fringes of the possible.

We joked and laughed non-stop, we shouted and jeered at motorists who honked their horns when we couldn't push the stroppy door the way we wanted it to go. We heaved the damn thing over Magdalene Bridge, constantly struggling to haul it out of the gutter, holding up buses, trucks, even cyclists. The door-mobile soon proved itself yet again as the most inefficient method of bulk transportation ever devised.

To top everything else, the clouds lifted that day and the weak spring sun caused the temperature to rise off the floor where it had lain dormant for so many months. We were dressed in leather jackets and big boots, cloaks and thick jumpers, long scarves and gloves. I was wearing the striped green long thin hat with a bell on the end of it, which Charlie had christened my 'tonk' hat, that being the sound it gave off every time I moved. As we lugged the unstable mass up the Cowley Road and heaved it up the final rise of Southfield Road, we actually broke into a sweat.

'Nearly there, man,' said Charlie as we shoved the door-mobile along a quiet suburban street. I saw the name, Hilltop Road. This was Hilltop: it was a normal road, it wasn't a castle. It was suburbia.

'Number 56,' said Charlie. 'Hope there's some milk in the fridge.'

The house was detached, but looked like it shouldn't have been. It was exactly the style of so many semi-detached houses that grace the streets of the slightly more up-market of Britain's suburbs. It was a turn-of-the-century town house, stone and red brick in a pleasing combination, with spacious bay windows, a small front garden with a big bush, and a drive down the side, leading to a garage. The front door, heavy and imposing, was down the side too.

'Shit, man. No one home,' said Charlie, who had rung the front doorbell. 'Never mind.'

Charlie's long thin legs seemed to span the decorative stonework up the front of the house as easily as a long-legged spider climbs woodchip wallpaper. There was barely a halt in his movements. He slid up the wall, clearly knowing the route well. He was up and in through the front bay window before I could say 'Far out'.

Moments later he came to the front door, drinking copiously from a bottle of milk. He burped and walked into the kitchen. The entrance hall smelt of polish: there were stairs leading up to a carpeted landing. I glanced in the front room as I followed Charlie: big furniture, fat sofa, large pot plants, thick armchairs and a ticking clock.

The kitchen was truly a proper kitchen, possibly the first I had ever seen: red quarry-tiled floor, well-built old pine furniture covered in highbrow broadsheet news-papers, built-in kitchen units, huge fridge, dishwasher, front-loading washing machine and tumble drier. My mum and dad had a top loader with an old table top to cover it when not in use.

Charlie was hacking huge slices off a loaf of fresh bread and cutting chunks of butter on to it. He wasn't even going through the rudimentary process of spreading, he was taking bread and butter into the new culinary realm of 'chunkdom'.

'Help yourself,' he said through an unfeasibly large mouthful. I sawed through the fresh-smelling loaf and loaded the slice with cheese, pickled beetroot and salami that I found in copious quantities in the fridge.

'This is too much,' I said as I stuffed my face and drank milk from another bottle. Charlie sat with one leg twitching, reading the paper. He turned the pages so fast he was either skipping through the stories or he was a frighteningly fast reader.

'Chocky cake?' said Charlie, getting up and lifting a tin off the top of the fridge. We demolished it in seconds, swallowing slabs of rich, almost black, chocolate gateau.

A key went in the front door. We sat mid-chew staring at each other. Then a schoolgirl walked in carrying an over-stuffed hand-woven Greek shoulder bag. She wore a white shirt, black tie, black tights and a Jean Machine denim skirt. It was the clogs that were the clue. Battered black clogs. It was the girl in the fur coat from the party. The long-stride girl who had left with the mop-haired boy.

'Carol, this is Robbie,' he said, muffled by a mouthful of cake.

'Charlie, you fucking bastard,' she said, looking into the empty cake tin. 'I wanted a piece of that.'

Charlie bent his head forward and allowed a large chunk of partially digested cake to plop into his open palm. He offered it to her with a chocolate-encrusted smile.

'Fuck that,' she said and walked out, kicking her clogs off and running upstairs.

'My sister,' said Charlie. 'Probably her time of the month. You know. Private girlie stuff. Best not to get involved.'

Charlie and I humped his chest and posters, Indian bedspreads and hippie trinkets up to his bedroom, a room I would have died rather than leave had it been mine. It was up in the eaves of the house and had a view from its ceiling-high windows of the city. That was my first real sighting of the city of dreaming spires; the sunlight caught the many pointed towers of the colleges in just the way I imagined people had gone on about for so long. You have to get out of the city to see this view: it is easy to live there and forget what a remarkably beautiful place it is.

Charlie went downstairs after the last load and I stared out of the window, smoking a cigarette. It made no sense to me for Charlie to leave this amazing room, with a fridge full of milk and tins full of chocolate gateaux. Leave all this and live in a condemned hovel on the other side of town?

'Can you spare a fag, Rob?' said a girl's voice. Charlie's sister had changed into a thin Indian cheesecloth shirt which was tantalizingly transparent.

'Yeah, yeah, sure,' I said, offering her the packet. She had called me Rob. She remembered my name.

'Fucking homework,' she said. 'Really pisses me off. The whole trip.'

'Yeah, it's bad,' I said. My eyes darted around the room trying not to look at her breasts. It became too hard, so I looked out of the window.

'Have you left school then?' she asked.

'Yeah. I was kicked out last year. Dope and *The Little Red School Book*.'

'Right,' said Carol as if this were par for the course.

'Where d'you go?' I asked.

'St Theresa's, just up the road. It's crap.'

'All schools are crap. Schools are prisons, really. I don't miss going. I got one O level, art. That was it.'

'I thought you were expelled.'

'Yeah, I was, but they let me back in to do my O levels. I failed seven. I refused to answer the fascist questions, but I was good at art. I'm a cartoonist.'

'Oh, right,' said Carol, flicking hair out of her eyes. 'Charlie's really good at cartoons. Mind you, Charlie's really good at everything.'

'He's still at school then?' I asked.

'Sometimes. When he bothers to go. He's supposed to be studying for his A levels, but he never does any work, then he sits his mocks and passes the lot. It's not fair. I'm trying to get my O levels, but I won't. It's shit.'

'So you're in the fifth form now?' I asked, trying to work out how old she was.

'Yeah, I want to go to tech college next year. I can't stand the uniform and the crappy teachers. Are you going to college?'

'Nah. I've been living in a commune in Wales till recently. I've dropped out pretty much. I live with some commune people now, near where the party was last night.'

'Right,' said Carol, clearly unimpressed by my commune credentials.

'Good party, though, until the police came.'

'That was totally heavy,' said Carol, drawing heavily on her cigarette. 'I was so pissed off.'

'Yeah, the pigs were really heavy.'

'No,' said Carol. 'Mark, the guy I was with, got me to carry his dope across town last night. He said he couldn't afford to get busted! What about me? Bastard!'

'Is he your boyfriend?' I asked as I scanned the skyline looking for something that would hold my attention for more than five seconds.

'Was,' she said, exhaling a cloud of smoke. 'It's been rocky for months. It's really over now. He's so fucked up. Lives with his dad, down there.' She pointed over to East Oxford. 'His elder brother's a dealer, in real big trouble. He's had to leave the country.'

'Wow, heavy!' I said.

'Yeah, he lives in Ireland, and Mark has had to sort out all his stuff, all the money and dope and everything, and it's all just too fucked up. I can't stand it.'

'No, sure,' I said, trying to sound sympathetic. I was in awe of her: only just sixteen and yet she knew these kinds of people. Dealers who'd had to flee the country, a boyfriend, or ex maybe, who was really fucked up. Although I might not have lived a conventional life, I always knew I wasn't really 'fucked up' like so many of my contemporaries. I always had clean socks and underpants, I always had a few pounds in my pocket. I didn't get stoned very often, never got drunk or got into fights or got arrested. Carol's boyfriend Mark was in many ways who I'd imagined I would become before I left home.

The phone rang and Carol looked around. I took the cheap opportunity and stared as much as I could. She was extraordinarily beautiful, with proper breasts, like in the magazines. Moments later Charlie came bounding over the banister. He didn't use the stairs: he'd climbed up the hand rail and used his over-long arms to haul himself directly up the stairwell. 'Carol, it's Mark, for you.'

'Shit,' said Carol and threw the hair out of her eyes

flamboyantly. She walked down the corridor with her big long strides, her hair waving in time with her steps.

'It's all got really heavy with Mark. His brother . . .' said Charlie, taking one of my cigarettes without asking.

'Yeah, Carol just told me.'

'Yeah, Mark's pretty fucked up.'

'Is he at school with you?'

'Mark. School. No way, man, he's right out there. Did all his O levels on acid.'

'Oh, wow! Did he pass!'

'Couldn't even write, man. He thought the pen was his mother, trapped in plastic. Totally heavy.'

Carol came back up the stairs. 'He's coming round, wants me to do him one last favour but I said fuck that. So he's going to ask you, Charlie. He says it's desperate, really, really desperate.'

'Oh, man,' said Charlie, burying his face in his hands. 'What's it going to be now?'

'Don't do it, Charlie,' said Carol. 'For fuck's sake don't do it. Just tell him to piss off.'

At 11.30 that night, Charlie and I were riding our bikes through the pitch black silence of a country lane. I had bike lights, Charlie had gears, so we compromised: I went in front and did the map reading. The map in question was drawn by Mark in a state of advanced fucked-upness while sitting, twitching, at Charlie's dad's kitchen table. It was scrawled on a sheet of *The Times*, the only paper we could find, using an orange crayon.

We had followed the map out of Oxford, along a narrow country lane, down a farm track, over a five-bar gate with a public footpath sign on it, then into Wytham Woods, just west of Oxford, at a specific tree along the path, which we found without much difficulty, when we had to turn left and walk fifty paces.

'This is crazy, man,' I hissed as we stumbled through undergrowth.

'Twenty-seven, twenty-eight,' said Charlie. It was so dark we couldn't see a thing. Charlie was carrying a garden trowel, the nearest thing to a shovel we could find in the garage. We were in search of buried treasure. 'Forty-nine, fifty,' said Charlie. 'Switch the bike light on.' I did so, but sod's law kicked into gear and the batteries started to fade. A dull yellow light leaked from the lamp, from which we could just make out a large tree. We looked for the runic symbol that Mark's brother had carved there.

'Yes, look!' said Charlie, pointing to an upside-down J carved into the bark of the oak.

'Bloody hell! I can't believe we found it.'

Charlie struck a Buddhist mantra style pose and said in a spiritual American accent, 'We could never find it; it found us.'

'Yeah, it guided us here with its pure force of love,' I said, using the same breathy American accent.

Charlie started digging at the base of the tree with the garden trowel. The earth was sticky and muddy, clogged with roots.

After half an hour the hole was about two feet deep and nothing had been revealed. I rubbed the mud off my hands on to my jeans. 'Maybe the police have carved runes on every tree to confuse us and they're waiting with guns and helicopters and search lights,' I said, feeling the blister that had erupted on my lily-white palm. Charlie cupped his hand and spoke through it like a loud hailer: 'We have you surrounded. Come out with your hands up, or we will be forced to open fire and blow you to shreds, muthafukkas!'

We both made machine gun and mortar noises for

about ten minutes as we continued to dig. We found nothing.

'We fucked up,' said Charlie. 'Or more likely, Mark did. He's only got half a brain left.'

'Too many drugs, man,' I said in a half-American whine. Then the trowel hit something that didn't sound like a rock. It was metal. We switched the light back on; its last flickering light showed us the corner of a green metal box. We scrabbled together in the dirt, slowly loosening the earth enough to extract a small army surplus ammunition case. I hauled it out of the hole. It was heavy. Charlie opened it and the smell hit us immediately. Inside, wrapped in silver foil, were seven kilos of prime Afghan Black, Gold Label hashish. Worth, well, a hell of a lot of money.

'Oh, wow!' I said, feeling suddenly very scared. 'That's too much.'

'Yeah, this is heavy, man,' said Charlie. 'We don't want to be carrying this for longer than we have to. Let's haul ass outa here.'

We made our stumbling way on foot through the woods back to where we thought our bikes were, though we couldn't find them for about half an hour. I was on the edge of panic all the time, cursing myself for having agreed to go along with this mad caper. This was serious criminal stuff: not a little bit of hash wrapped in silver foil, but seven bloody kilos. We finally fell over the bikes by accident. Charlie had brought his dad's rucksack with him, and we loaded the ammo box into it and Charlie slung it over his shoulders. We started the ride back into Oxford, and when we came under the first street lights on the edge of suburbia, I could see that we looked terrible. I was covered from head to foot in mud, as was Charlie. We were begging to be stopped and searched by the police.

All the way through Oxford we didn't say a word to each other. We pedalled fast and hard through the now near-deserted streets, stopping at traffic lights and wiping our muddy hands on our filthy trousers. Why a passing patrol car didn't stop us I'll never know. We saw three, and each time I almost added to the mire that was on my jeans.

We got back to Hilltop Road without incident. Throwing the bikes down in the garage, kicking our mud-caked boots off, we went through the internal back door. The lights were on low in the kitchen. Carol and Mark were sitting at the large pine table, smoking cigarettes.

'Charlie!' said Carol, looking at us open-mouthed. 'What the fuck have you done?' She saw us, covered in sticky light brown mud, twigs and leaves. Our hair looked matted and rat's taily, just like the men in *We are Every-where*. We were frozen, we'd been cycling for what seemed like hours through the bitter night air, soaked to the skin. We were both smiling wildly.

'Boom Shanka,' said Charlie, holding up the ammo box. Mark walked up to him with small quick steps which reminded me of Mick Jagger crossing a stage during a guitar riff.

'Thanks, Charlie,' he said. 'Patrick won't forget, man. Okay, I'd better go.' Without even looking inside, Mark took the ammo box and walked out of the kitchen. He and Carol exchanged some hushed conversation, then we heard the door close and Carol came back in.

'It's all so fucked up,' said Carol. 'This is really serious, Charlie. You got busted last night, and now you're carrying tons of dope across town looking like that. God, if you'd got stopped, Dad wouldn't have been able to get you off.'

'Yeah, yeah,' said Charlie, who had already opened the

fridge and started downing milk. Carol stormed out of the kitchen and slammed her door. I felt very awkward.

'Don't worry, man. Have a bath. You can stay here tonight, in the spare room.'

That night I sat in the small spare bedroom, the strains of Janis Joplin coming creeping through the wall from Carol's room. In one day my life had spun off again in a completely new direction. I had only just met these people and yet I seemed to have been sucked into their lives. Carol was so beautiful. She made me really tense when I was near her, in case I said the wrong thing and she hated me. She seemed to have quite a temper, but that I found strangely attractive. And where was their father? There was no sign of him at the house.

I looked out of my window at the night-time spires of Oxford. It felt romantic. I wanted to be with Carol, or someone, but in a way, for that particular night, it was wonderful to be alone, quiet, safe in this big warm house on the hill.

9

Fox-fur Bed Cover

In the week before my birthday, for some reason which has forever eluded me, I had a cup of tea and a bacon sandwich in the Woolworths café on Cornmarket. It wasn't a salubrious joint – in fact it's since been pulled down and rebuilt – but in 1973 it was cheap and proletarian, it was warm and you could always get a seat. Considering how cold everywhere else was, it was rather attractive. I was probably buying drawing paper and pens with the intention of starting my own revolutionary cartoon newspaper and felt a bit peckish. I sat down opposite a man who smiled and said, 'Hello.'

He was very friendly and asked me about myself. I explained exactly who I was and what my life quest was for at least an hour, and eventually I found out he was a leather worker. He made bags, belts, pouches, wristbands and watch-straps out of leather and sold them to shops in Oxford, Reading and London.

'Sounds brilliant,' I said. His name was David, he was a lot older than me, not an obvious hippie, not an obvious anything really, just a bloke called David who actually worked for himself.

'I've always wanted to work for myself,' I said. 'I don't ever want another job. I've just finished working in the kitchens at Brasenose.'

'You could work with me,' he said. 'I'd teach you how to make stuff, pay you for what you make. Eventually I could sell you leather so you could make your own stuff.'

'Fantastic!'

'You won't make a fortune, but you can make a living,' said David flatly. He was so realistic. He wasn't like me, or Charlie, or the urban peasants or the man at the social security office in the cheap suit. He didn't seem to have an axe to grind, he just worked, got money, lived on it. It seemed so simple.

We arranged for me to visit his workshop just off the Iffley Road.

I was still living with Gary and Helen on my birthday. Cabbage woke me up and somehow I did feel special. There was a special feeling I used to experience, which wore off as I grew up. There were still traces of it when I was seventeen, a feeling of bright possibility, almost like a drug-induced state, the feeling that there was something good and rich hovering above, a chance around a corner, a surprise, a golden gift of hope somewhere. I got up and put on clean clothes. I'd had a bath the night before and felt that special, tingly clean feeling that you can only know if you cut your baths down to a shocking rarity.

There was a card on the hall floor when I went downstairs, 'Happy Birthday dear, lots of love from Mum and Dad.' I felt guilty about my parents for the first time since I'd moved away. I had left home so abruptly, and the card had a certain innocent poignancy. I had seen the same handwriting on each birthday card ever since I could remember. The writing pulled at me. It whispered, 'You are still our child, even if you leave home and hardly say good-bye, even if you dash our hopes of having a son with hair like Prince Charles and a tweed jacket with elbow patches, even if you dig up dope in the woods in the middle of the night and drink in a pub with a lot of semi-criminals, you are still our child.'

The card rested awkwardly on my lap as I sat down.

'Happy birthday,' said Gary, pouring tea in the back room of the now more comfortable urban-peasant house. We even had a lampshade and a television. Daisy was sitting on the carpet in front of the coal fire, playing quietly with a plastic cup and saucer.

'Thanks,' I said and drank some tea.

'Only seventeen,' said Gary. 'Make the most of it, Rob.' I nodded. I wanted to.

That night I went to a disco, the first since I'd left home and school. Charlie had told me to go there. 'Everybody'll be there, man,' he'd said. It was held in an upstairs room of St Mary the Virgin Church, right outside the gates of Brasenose. Right opposite the Radcliffe Camera, right slap bang in the middle of Oxford. The disco was run by the vicar and attracted a large crowd of long-haired, dope-smoking teenagers, who, as I got to know them, turned out to be the children of the academic élite of Oxford.

Carol and Charlie's father was Professor of Law at New College and had just finished his year as a proctor of the university, Mike's father was the managing director of a London-based international charity, Sarah's father was Professor of History at All Souls, Tim's father was Professor of Philosophy at Magdalene. They all thought their parents were wastrels, hypocrites, liars, cheats, philanderers. I learned this in the side room at the disco, where this product of academic breeding sat around and talked, smoked copious amounts of cigarettes and drank soft drinks. The disco at St Mary's was clearly their weekend get together.

The vicar wasn't stupid though. There were Christians at the disco: young, almost long-haired, enthusiastic Christians. They wore casual shirts and bulky sweaters, sensible warm clothes for a British winter. Not like our ripped denim, see-through shirts and battered leather jackets. They would sit near us and try and join in the conversation, which, since we were talking about smoking dope and how there is supposed to be a strain of grass in South Africa which is so strong it makes you blind, was quite difficult for them.

Mike was telling me that taking as many drugs as possible as young as possible was his main goal in life.

'But what do you believe in?' asked a Christian, with major eye contact. Mike laughed and looked away.

I took a deep breath and said, 'Total revolution, cultural revolution with a complete removal and destruction of the ruling élite, a return to an agrarian way of life, the abolition of motorized transport, land ownership reform and the legalization of dope.'

This response, in case a Christian ever corners you when you've other things on your mind, will silence them for a while, but not long.

'Would God feature in this revolution of yours?' he asked after a while.

'No way,' I said. 'All religions are a form of cultural oppression, used by the ruling class to crush the masses. All religions would be brutally outlawed, all Church buildings would be either destroyed or put to better use, all professional religious figures like vicars, priests, bishops and all that, they'd be publicly hanged.' I smiled as I said this, but the Christian remained fairly poker-faced.

'I want to get totally smashed out of my fucking brains for every living second of my life. That's what I believe in,' said Mike. He got up and beckoned me. 'Come on,' he said. 'Let's go and dance.'

We entered the main room, where a Status Quo single was running through its familiar routine. Mike and I stood facing each other, put our thumbs in our belt loops, placed our feet wide apart and swung our shoulders from side to side in rhythm with the music. Then, on every fourth beat, we would dive our heads down, hopefully in opposite directions, because in order to flick the hair correctly, this head dive had to be done at great speed. We'd do a double dip in time with the music, and then back up. For some reason, Mike and I, who had little else in common, could do this head bangers' dance to a very high standard.

'That was fucking amazing,' said Carol when the record had finished. She was standing with three other girls her age: two with long skinny legs like hers, and one who was a little bit heavier. 'Come and meet my friends.' She took my hand and led me towards them. They were all checking me out and I'm sure I blushed.

'This is Rob, he's a leather worker,' said Carol. 'This is Anna' (father: Professor of Biochemistry, Corpus Christi; mother: Head of Linguistics Department, Lady Margaret Hall) 'and this is Rosie' (father: Director of Experimental Child Psychology, Green College).

'Your legs are so thin,' said Carol.

'Yeah, fantastic,' said Rosie. She laughed. I liked her. The other two were being a bit too pouty and sulky for my taste.

'I had hepatitis,' I lied. 'Last year, when I was living in a commune.'

'Rob used to live in a commune in Wales,' said Carol proudly.

'Oh, fantastic!' said Rosie, 'Where was it?'

'Llanbedr, in the Black Mountains.'

'Oh, far out!' trilled Rosie. 'I'm desperate to live in a commune. I'm still stuck at home with my stupid mother and dad. They barely let me come here.'

'Rosie's mum's really strict,' said Carol.

'What about your mum?' I asked her.

'Oh, she fucked off when we were kids; she lives in America.' She held my arm again and looked around the room, then she stood very close and spoke into my ear. 'Don't mention our mum to Charlie, he's really fucked up about it.'

'Okay,' I said, and nodded knowingly. Carol started talking to Sarah and I tried not to stare at her too much. The intimacy of having her whisper in my ear had stayed with me.

'How old are you, Rob?' asked Rosie, with a big grin.

'Seventeen,' I said. 'Today.'

'Oh, wow!' screamed Rosie. 'Carol, it's Rob's seventeenth birthday!'

Carol turned and smiled with a gleaming row of perfect white teeth. 'Fantastic!' she said. 'Happy birthday.'

'It's Carol's birthday next week,' said Rosie. 'We should have a party!'

'Tonight,' said Carol. 'Up at Hilltop. Dad's still away.'

'Fantastic!' said Rosie. 'I'll tell everyone.' She moved off through the crowd.

'Coming?' Carol said to me with a delicious grin.

'Sure,' I said.

We both laughed. The Doobie Brothers' song 'Jesus is Just Alright' was playing – very appropriate for a church disco. I stared at Carol, she stared at me and at the same time, without hesitation from either side, we moved together and kissed. Her eyes sparkled afterwards and we both had to smoke a lot of cigarettes to cover our nervousness and embarrassment.

At midnight I was sitting on Carol's bedroom floor rolling a joint. The Doors were playing on her stereo. Charlie was trying to make pancakes in the kitchen with a lot of laughing, noisy young people watching and joking.

Carol told me Mike and Anna were 'doing it' in the front room, so we shouldn't go in there. Rosie, Sarah and Carol were in her room with the odd passing long-hair, Gollum being one of them.

'Evening all,' he said, as he poked his head around the door.

'Gollum!' screamed Rosie.

'Hello, Rosie. Fancy a kiss?' Gollum smiled like a lizard.

'Oh, yuk!' screamed Rosie. Gollum shrank away. 'So creepy,' said Rosie, and all the girls dissolved into fits of laughter. I was smiling, but feeling slightly sorry for Gollum.

By two in the morning, a lot of people had drifted away and, due to the fact that she had purloined the family stereo system, the remainder congregated in Carol's room. Rosie had grilled me for an hour on what living in a commune was like, and I was able to lie fluently.

'We decided to reject all forms of, like, mechanical devices, and get back to a sort of medieval method of farming.'

'Brilliant!' said Rosie. Carol was slightly less impressed.

'So we only used horse-drawn carts and stuff.'

'I love riding,' said Carol.

I had the lie meter up full. 'Oh, well, my mum's got a horse,' I said. 'You'll have to come out some weekend and you can have a ride.'

'Brilliant!' said Carol.

'Boom Shanka,' said Charlie, holding up a giant joint. It must have been three feet long. We all burst out laughing. Someone put a Pentangle album on the stereo, and the conversation buzzed. Rosie and Carol exchanged glances. I said, 'What?' and they both laughed. It was a moment of exquisite insecurity, hovering on the edge of understanding. These two girls seemed to know far more about what was going on in that room than I did. I had spent the previous year of my life learning how to be cool, how to survive through the difficulties of adolescence without letting anyone know you weren't sure what was going on. Which I wasn't.

Finally, bored with waiting for me to suggest something, Carol stood up and beckoned me to the door. I stood up too, feeling very embarrassed, knowing everyone was looking at us. I knew what was coming and I wasn't overly excited about it. I found Carol extremely attractive but I knew sex wasn't going to be straightforward. I had spent enough time with Allie to know that it wasn't an automatic process.

Outside, on the landing, she kissed me full on the lips. It was lovely. We kissed for ages, standing awkwardly in the no man's land of the stairwell.

After an hour of full snogging, Carol took me into her father's bedroom, closer to my original castle-on-the-hill fantasy than I would have ever dared expect. Even the turn of her body as she held my hand and walked in front of me was just as I had pictured it. She wasn't wearing a long velvet dress, there weren't burning brands held in iron clasps on the bare stone walls, but it was close enough.

It's safe to say this bedroom was not what I had come to expect from the bedrooms of my friends' parents. There was a huge, king-size double bed with an animal fur quilt, made of hundreds of furs joined together in a vast sheet.

'Fox,' said Carol, seeing me transfixed by the sight. There was an angled mirror, three feet high, attached to the wall as a headboard. There were loads of soft, satin-type pillows scattered on it. It was a bed clearly and openly made for having sex on.

Now, whatever process of storytelling, embellishment, downright lies and deceptions I have been revealing on these pages, there is one cast iron fact: this Professor of Law at Oxford University, world-respected expert in contract and matrimonial law, had a bed that was kinky as fuck.

I was so taken aback by it I walked around looking at everything else. It was decorated with bookshelves and pot plants, large old wardrobes and rich-smelling curtains. This was unlike any room I had ever been in, rich and thick with knowledge and experience. Experience of other countries, other times in history, other ways of life that weren't either middle-class suburban or wild Black Mountain hippie.

Carol took off her T-shirt just like the thousands of pictures I'd seen in men's magazines. Just like the thousands of fantasies I'd had about girls doing just that. T-shirt over the head, breasts revealed for the first time, result in all heterosexual men on earth: stiffy. Result in yours truly: a desire to talk about anything other than sex.

She pulled off her jeans and lay on the bed, semi-naked. I sat in an ornate rocking chair on the other side of the large bedroom and looked at her. She wrapped her extraordinary beauty in the giant fur thing and smiled at me. Here was every seventeen-year-old boy's fantasy: a sexually precocious sixteen year old, who wasn't a virgin, who was lying naked, except for some very small knickers, on her father's bed, which was covered in fur.

Did we writhe together in primal, lustful ecstasy, making love nineteen times in one night in a fevered passionate frenzy? No. I talked and she fell asleep. Once I realized this, I went back into her bedroom, where the hardcore dopers were still just about going, and sat down, smiling. They all smiled at me, assuming I had just performed top quality sex and needed a smoke afterwards.

A week later, in the quiet privacy of her room, with Janis Joplin's 'Me and Bobby McGee' playing softly on her stereo, I managed to achieve coitus with Carol. It was very romantic, very touching and very private really. For all her social bravura and semi-nudity at school, Carol was an intensely private and shy person.

So many words have been written about first sexual experiences, or any old sexual experiences, and in so many ways that I have no desire to add to them. I only want to record that it was one of the bigger disappointments of my life. It certainly wasn't Carol's fault. I was too young at seventeen. Men are a bit slow anyway, and I was slower than most. My education had left me totally bereft of any framework or language into which I could place all the feelings which came along with the sexual intimacy.

I was hopelessly unprepared for the whole thing. My only education was smutty jokes with other boys, pornography – which leaves you utterly misinformed – and truly appalling sex education at school.

I had no idea it was going to be so emotional. All the information I had received had led me to expect a sort of distant pummelling sensation, with the girl over there in the corner where you could look at her and 'fancy' her, and go 'phwoooar' because she was naked and had breasts and nice thighs. Yet it was all so close, and it was so close for so long. There were so many other things to take into consideration when you first have sex. Breath, hair, bedding that gets twisted up, the sounds, the immense discomfort of holding yourself above a girl when your arms are pipe-cleaner thin and dry-twig weak.

10

Hilltop Safety

'A geodesic dome!' said Charlie, late one night in his back bedroom at Hilltop Road. He pulled out a sheet of clean paper and started to draw.

'Yeah, it's this structure for unsupported dwelling spaces,' I said, 'developed by this American professor bloke called Richard Buckminster Fuller.'

'Yeah, yeah,' said Charlie, drawing a geodesic dome with amazing speed and accuracy. 'D'you know what geodesic means?'

'Like a dome.'

'Geodesic is the shortest distance between two points on a curved surface. A geodesic on a sphere is an arc of a great circle.'

'Oh yeah, that's it. Buckminster Fuller always goes on about great circles,' I said.

'A great circle being a circle on a sphere whose plane passes through the centre of the sphere.'

'Yeah. More or less,' I said, feeling a little deflated. 'That's the basic idea. I made one when I was still at school. Out of cardboard.'

'Far out!' said Charlie. 'Did you live in it?'

'Well, no, the school used it for storing sports equipment during the summer, after I was expelled.'

'Far out! Well, we should build another one.'

'Yeah, I'd love to,' I said. 'But I'm broke and I've got to make wristbands.'

'Wristbands! Heavy,' said Charlie, who was wearing one. He had untwisted it and re-plaited it within nine seconds of me giving it to him. Took me nearly a week to learn how to do it.

Most of my time had become devoted to making leather wristbands for David in Iffley. I became a dab hand at their manufacture. I could produce many hundreds of them a day. My fingers were perpetually stained from the dye, the polish and the damp leather. My back ached from the hours I spent, sitting on a battered chair, in front of a slice of tree which acted as my work bench, cutting, bevelling, twisting, twiddling, dyeing, polishing and hole punching plaited leather wristbands. I hope you bought one once. They were made with love.

The wrist straps were simple affairs. Take a strip of leather seven or eight inches long and half an inch wide. Cut two parallel incisions down the length of the strip, without going through to the ends. You see, this was the trick, they looked impossible. Both ends of the wristband were solid leather, and the centre part was plaited. How did we do that? It is a secret of the leather-working brotherhood and I would die a horrible death if I were to divulge this holy knowledge.

Once they were finished and fitted with a ring spring fastener at both ends, I would string vast collections of them together and throw them over my shoulder. I'd don my leather jacket and beret, my old boots and slightly flared, heavily patched jeans, and catch the bus to Oxford train station. I would buy a return ticket for four pounds and I would then accompany David the leather worker from Iffley to London. We'd get out at Paddington, catch the tube – two human leather hedgehogs, with leather accessories for spines – and head for Carnaby Street, Kensington Market, the King's Road and Camden High Street, where we would distribute our wares.

David would also have a load of bags, belts and pouches

which were likewise left, usually on a sale or return basis, in some of London's hipper shops.

Once this was complete, we would retire to a small Soho eatery, often Jimmy's basement café in Frith Street, were we would eat a huge, Greek chicken dinner with a lot of raw cabbage, costing about seventy-five pence.

We would then catch the number 38 up Tottenham Court Road and get off near Euston Station. Then a short walk to the old Connolly leather warehouse on Chalton Street. Now converted into trendy offices and apartments, it was a charming, musty old joint in 1973. The smell of leather, for some reason a rich and comfortable smell, would engulf us as we passed the heavy wooden entrance doors. I dreamt of whole houses covered in leather, I dreamt of living in Connolly's leather warehouse and making really beautiful leather things, almost leather sculpture, intricate, minutely stitched and ethnic in an Afghan sort of way. Lots of beautiful polishing, bevelling and deep red colours.

We'd climb the broad, well-swept wooden stairs to the top floor where, under the large span of the old wooden eaves, we would buy bellies. Dozens of them. The belly is the sort of scrag-end of leather cut from, well, a cow's belly. It's the bits they cut off the good hides. These were six foot long strips, about two feet wide at the most. They looked a bit like sun-dried fish, big sun-dried fish. The old man in the khaki overalls would place his roll-up cigarette carefully on the wooden bench, near the dozens of burn marks, roll the bellies we'd chosen carefully into a large hoop, wrap them in brown paper and tie them with stout string. We'd then have to go through the Dickensian process of actually paying for them, taking his chitty down to the first floor, holding other chitties in various deserted corridors, waiting for squat, rotund old ladies who smelt of lavender to type out beautiful old receipts on a manual typewriter. It was a day's work buying £25 worth of leather, but I loved it. We'd then catch the afternoon train back to Oxford and start the whole process again.

I had just come back from London earlier in the evening, and had wandered up to Hilltop Road to see Carol. She'd been looking after Cabbage for me while I was away. Cabbage was asleep in her bedroom, so was Carol. I was unable to sleep and got up to talk to Charlie, who rarely seemed to sleep at night.

'You know what Fat Freddy says,' said Charlie, referring to the Gilbert Shelton, Furry Freak Brothers cartoon character. 'Dope will get you through times of no money better than money will get you through times of no dope.'

He lit up a small joint from his ashtray collection. I puffed on it, but not with any great relish. I was depressed about my living situation. Although I hadn't actually moved out of Gary and Helen's house on St Bernards Road, I was more or less living at Charlie's dad's house. However, I knew I was living on borrowed time. Charlie's dad was going to come back sometime with his new wife. I would have to go. It had all been too pleasant, to work at David's house in Iffley, ride my bike back to Hilltop Road in the evening, drink milk, eat fresh bread, have baths with Carol, make love, then get up and sit in Charlie's room and talk about domes.

'I want to go build a dome out on Port Meadow,' I said to Charlie. 'On a raised base made of wooden pallets.'

'Trippy,' said Charlie.

'Yeah. In the end I want to set up a huge geodesic community, which is really a university. Maybe in Wales, with some of the domes thousands of feet high, so it's, like, whole halls of residence all in one huge dome.'

'Too much!' said Charlie.

'But to start with, I'd just build it, like, overnight, yeah, then in the morning, claim squatter's rights, live out there with Cabbage, go hunting with a bow and arrow.'

'Or a crossbow,' said Charlie. 'They're amazing. A 300-pound crossbow can fire a bolt through a brick wall.'

'Brilliant!'

'Tell you what,' said Charlie. 'You could build a dome really cheaply. There's a building site down the road, we could go and reclaim some materials from there and start building right away.'

'What, like liberate big spars of timber and build, say, a ninety foot high dome?'

'Yeah, man. Far out. Let's go and liberate some materials from capitalist land speculators. This way.'

Charlie stood in a super-hero pose for a moment, threw his cloak on, lifted the sash window in his room and climbed out on to the small tiled roof that went over the kitchen extension. I followed him, carefully putting my booted foot where his bare ones had been. I was getting the same, 'Don't think about it, do it!' feeling of elation I had experienced on our bike ride to pick up the hash stash in the forest. The daftest, most stupid, least logical, most dangerous and hardest to justify task had an immense pull. Charlie dropped to the ground and started walking down the small back garden. He was already over the fence and in the field at the back before I had managed to get off the roof. As I looked into the empty kitchen I thought that it would have been a lot easier to go down the stairs and out of the back door, but this already felt like an adventure.

I caught up with Charlie as we wandered over the field, the distant street lights giving us just enough light to see. Over one more field and we entered a huge area of house building sites: great piles of bricks, pre-made timber roof

166

trusses, diggers and tippers were all strewn about in the mud.

'There's nothing here,' I said, despondently looking at the muddy puddles and shards of broken timber on the ground. I think I had been expecting huge supplies of thick wooden spars thrown on a waste heap which we could just take the following morning.

'Aha,' said Charlie, lifting a huge long thing from one end.

'What is it?' I said, peering through the gloom.

'Plastic sheeting, man. They use it to make a damp-proof course. It's really thick, just what you need for a dome.'

'Brilliant!' I said. 'What do we do?'

'Give us a hand. We'll carry it back.'

'But, well,' I said, my morals under stress, 'I don't know.'

It's not that I'd never stolen anything before in my life. I had pinched sweets from the local newsagent when I was ten; a boy I was at school with had got caught stealing a toy car with me when I was twelve and I spent the weekend in a living hell thinking he was going to tell the police my name. He didn't, and the store didn't press charges, but the feeling was not good. Now I was looking at a ten foot roll of plastic sheeting on a building site in East Oxford, something I would really like, something which suddenly made a huge geodesic dome a possibility.

'Come on, man,' said Charlie. 'The company doing these buildings is making millions every year. They're not even going to notice. It's only a roll of plastic.'

'Yeah,' I said, grabbing the end and lifting it. 'And anyway, they steal from people by running a capitalist economy based on profit.'

'Yeah, man,' said Charlie laughing. 'They deserve to be ripped off.' Charlie did his slow druggy laugh and we hauled the roll of plastic back up through the field to his house. We pole-vaulted it over the back fence and heard Cabbage yelp.

'Oh, shit!' I said and jumped up to look over the back fence. Cabbage was sniffing the great roll. It had clearly frightened the life out of the poor dog but had not injured her. 'She's okay,' I said and we climbed into the garden. Back in the kitchen, Carol came downstairs wearing a big T-shirt. She looked sleepy and very cute.

'What's all the fucking noise?' she asked, clearly not too pleased.

'We've liberated some plastic sheeting,' I said. 'For a geodesic dome I'm going to build on Port Meadow.'

'Robbie's going to live in it and hunt for things with Cabbage, using a bow and arrow,' said Charlie pouring some badly made tea into unwashed mugs.

'Or a crossbow,' I said. 'A 300-pound bolt can go through a stone wall.'

'No, it's a 300-pound bow,' said Charlie. 'Three hundred pounds is the breaking strain of the steel bow that propels the bolt. The bolt itself only weighs a few ounces.'

'Oh, wow. A 300-pound bolt wouldn't go so far,' I said, miming a giant bolt sliding off the end of a crossbow and falling on my foot. I hopped around the kitchen in mock agony with Cabbage jumping up trying to bite my wrist and join in.

'What have you taken?' asked Carol, lighting a cigarette. I laughed.

'Nothing,' I said. 'We just went down to the building site and ripped off this huge roll of plastic. It was brilliant.'

'We're high on crime,' said Charlie, drawing furiously on a sheet of paper he'd found on the table.

'I think you're fucking mad,' said Carol. 'What's a geodesic dome, for God's sake? Why don't you stay here?'

'I can't stay here for ever,' I said. 'Your dad's going to turn up soon. He won't want me here.'

'He won't mind,' said Carol. 'It's his wife that's the problem.'

'She's all right,' said Charlie without looking up. Carol and Charlie didn't discuss their family very often, and I was intrigued by the sound of their stepmother. My mind flashed to his dad's bed, the one with the mirror that I couldn't sleep with Carol in. Somehow the image of a stepmother, something I connected with *The Sound of Music*, didn't quite match the image of the big front bedroom.

'Where is she?' I asked.

'She's staying with her mum in London. They fell out, I don't know. My dad's a bit like Charlie. Crazy, always going off and doing something weird.'

'There you go,' said Charlie. He had drawn the front page of a comic book. It had jaggedy writing at the top which said 'Teenagers High On Crime'. Underneath was a picture of me and Charlie stealing a long roll of plastic sheeting under a smiling moon. I had a speech bubble coming out of my mouth which said, 'Oh wow, the colours.' Charlie had a speech bubble which said, 'Pant, pant, I need more crime to get high.' It was very funny.

'You should get them published,' said Carol looking at the drawing. 'Both of you are really good at cartoons, you should get them all published or something. You'd make loads of money.' She stubbed out her cigarette and went back upstairs. Charlie and I sat around drawing cartoons for about an hour, sitting mostly in silence, completely forgetting the large roll of plastic in the back garden. I went to bed very late, Cabbage followed me up the stairs, I crawled in behind Carol and Cabbage crawled in behind me. It was very safe and quiet in the house, comfortable and easy. Had I been physically in tune, I would have known that this period of peace in my life was a clear sign that things were about to get seriously out of hand.

Carol and Charlie's dad did indeed appear about three days later. He was tall and slim and much younger looking than I expected. Charlie did look quite like him. The professor was funny and light-hearted, and immediately became very fond of Cabbage.

'Cabbage. That's a very odd name for a dog, isn't it?' he said stroking her grateful head. 'Hello there, Cabbage. And what do you want? A biscuit?'

'Rob's building a geodesic dome on Port Meadow, Dad,' said Carol, who was washing up. She had a job on her hands since we hadn't managed to find time to do it for weeks.

'How very enterprising. Have you got planning permission?' he asked. I remembered he was a professor of law, so he was bound to ask something like that.

'It's common land,' I said. 'You can squat on it legally.'

'Can you indeed? I'd love to read the statute which states that so clearly,' he said with a high-pitched giggle. He stood up and looked around. 'Well, I must say, children, you have looked after the house very well. Haven't they, Cabbage?'

'Yeah, well, we're like, really responsible, man,' said Charlie, with his hair pulled over his eyes.

'Oh Charlie, please don't do that,' said the professor. 'It's bad enough seeing you with all that dreadful hair without you looking like a yeti. When did you last wash it, by the way?'

'Hair washing's fascist. Ask Robbie,' said Charlie.

'Well, I don't know,' I said.

'Hair washing is fascist, Cabbage. What d'you think of that?' said the professor, picking up his suitcase and heading upstairs. Cabbage stayed with him, looking up at his long, bespectacled face. 'You come up with me and have a look around my room. There're lots of your little friends on my bed, Cabbage, lots of foxes. Cabbage. That's a very odd name for a dog, but it suits you somehow.'

I stayed at Hilltop Road that night, only I slept in the tiny spare room with the view of the spires. I could see Carol's window, her light still on. It seemed very odd that I wasn't in there with her. When Cabbage climbed up the stairs with me she chose to sleep in Carol's room, ignoring my clicks and whistles. Maybe I could carry on living there. It seemed like the ideal compromise: to have left home, be an adult and yet have a really nice house to live in, where everything was paid for and there was a really friendly mad old professor who wasn't that mad or old, who dropped in every now and then and made us tidy up.

'Look, there's some of my wristbands,' I said to Carol as we walked along the King's Road in Chelsea. Her father had given her some money for her birthday, which was only a week after mine, so he was a little late. By about a month. But it's the thought that counts. We decided to go shopping in London. Carol wanted an Afghan dress she had seen in a shop on the King's Road and we were going to have a look. Rosie, Carol's friend, came with us. It was almost sunny as we strolled along the tree-lined street, crossed the road at the traffic lights and entered the up-market hippie emporium.

I was bedazzled by the displays of heavily brocaded cloths, embroidered boots and crusty, cracking old leather work. Afghan clothes were the hippest of the hip in 1973. Bianca Jagger wore stuff like this, models in *Vogue* magazine stood near poor people in deserts wearing Afghan clothes. Carol could have been a model except that being a model was fucked as far as she was concerned. Most things were fucked as far as she was concerned, but she wanted the dress.

In the basement was yet more stuff: bags and big, thickly quilted long dresses, with masses of heavy embroidery and beadwork. Carol tried two dresses on. The first, while very nice, was a bit plain and dull. The second was extraordinary. Rosie admired her in it.

'You look fantastic,' she said. 'You look totally fantastic. It really, really suits you, Carol.'

Carol stood in front of a mirror; a balding man in a T-shirt hovered casually in the background. 'I don't know,' said Carol. 'It's sort of what I want.' She spun around in it, the dress tinkled as if covered in a million tiny bells. Tiny lead weights were sewn to the bottom hem which made it hang heavy and ethnic.

'How much is it?' she asked the balding man.

'Ninety pounds,' he said as if it were the most reasonable price ever mentioned for a dress someone else had made in another country who had no money and had sold this one for five bob.

'Right,' said Carol as she continued to admire herself in the mirror. The balding man started talking to another customer and Carol went back into the changing room. 'I think I like the other one better,' she said to me through the door. She peeked out, naked except for her pants. 'Give me your bag,' she hissed. I looked around and my heart rate went through the roof. Rosie's face flushed as if it had been re-sprayed.

'What are you going to do?' I pleaded, my voice wavering.

'Nick the fucker, what d'you think.'

I handed her my leather bag. It was the first one I had made under David's supervision. It was round and bulky, and after hastily removing some of the odds and ends from it which we transferred to Rosie's woven Greek shoulder bag, Carol unceremoniously stuffed the most beautiful dress inside.

Carol handed the bag to me and came out of the dressing room in her standard issue jeans, sweat shirt and ripped fur coat. She put the remaining dress back on the counter and smiled at the balding man as we left. He smiled back, not interrupting his conversation with the other woman he was serving. Carol dawdled in the shop upstairs, presumably so as not to attract attention, but Rosie and I were incredibly nervous, particularly me as I had £90 worth of stolen goods stuffed in my now bulging leather bag.

We got outside the shop and casually crossed the road.

'That was fucking amazing!' said Rosie. 'Oh wow, Carol. That was really far out!'

'Yeah,' said Carol. 'Brilliant!'

'Oh, shit,' I said. I had made the lucky mistake of glancing back at the shop. The bald man was already on the street, trying to cross over the busy road. He was waving at us, not aggressively, very much like an honest shopkeeper would do if you'd left your change on the counter.

I started running. I could run fast. I ran so fast I was overtaking buses and taxis crawling along the King's Road. Carol could clearly run quite well but she was hampered by her clogs. Rosie, to be honest, couldn't run at all.

'Meet you in the women's toilets, Sloane Square,' shouted Carol as I left her jogging along the pavement. I didn't look around to see if he was behind me, or if he caught Carol. I just ran as fast as I could, not looking when I crossed side streets, just relying on speed alone to get me through.

As I locked the compartment in the women's toilets I

realized I couldn't really see. I was so short of breath, my chest hurt so much and my heart was making externally visible movements through my clothes that I was sure I was about to die.

'Rob,' said Carol's voice from outside. I opened the door. She was smiling with her wonderful teeth. 'Fuck me, you can run fast,' she said and gave me a hug. From that day to this, Carol has never, ever worn that beautiful and hard-won dress. She just wanted it, she just had to have it, and she had better things to spend her money on, so she stole it. Or I stole it for her.

The problem with theft is that the difference between getting away with it and getting caught is universally huge. If you get away with it, you feel so omnipotent, so clearly superior to everyone else milling around being good that it all seems worth it. If you get caught, you shrivel up and die inside, looking back on the unspeakable stupidity of what you've done, wishing only that you could return to that moment of decision and choose not to steal. As I was running down the King's Road, I could see the dress hanging on the rack, unstolen. I wished so hard that it were still there, and that I were just walking along the road, happy and free. But, as we caught the tube back to Paddington station, I felt so good.

'You were brilliant, Rob,' said Rosie. 'The way you ran, it was amazing. The bloke just gave up. He could see he had no way of catching you.'

'Yeah, and your legs are so thin,' said Carol.

'Yeah, brilliant!' said Rosie.

Thin legs were clearly *de rigueur* amongst the North Oxford set. I was relishing the attention. I felt like I existed, like people were interested in me, in my long hair and thin legs.

'Yeah, well, I had hepatitis when I lived in Wellington

Square,' I said, embroidering the truth with skill. 'So I got really, really thin. I weighed only six stone at one time.'

'Brilliant!' said Carol, herself a waif.

'Did you use to live in Wellington Square?' said Rosie.

'Yeah.'

'With the Global Village Trucking Company?' she screamed, so that the commuters surrounding us glanced our way. Rosie was referring to a band which was loosely connected with Oxford, and some of whom had lived in one of the squats in Wellington Square.

'Oh, yeah,' I lied. 'We all had hepatitis, it was really heavy, but yeah, I know the Globs.' I'd heard people refer to them in this way.

'Oh, wow! That's amazing.'

On the train to Oxford we pulled the dress from my bag. 'It's so beautiful,' said Carol, holding it up to herself.

'Ripping stuff off is weird,' I said. I wanted to talk about it but I didn't know how. I felt uncomfortable, but it was so hip to steal things it was embarrassing to admit my disquiet. Rosie was nodding, Carol was looking at her dress.

'I know ripping off big companies is cool, because they steal from us, and they steal from the Third World and they're just organized rip-off gangs. And banks and that, they all deserve to rot, or be utterly ripped off.'

'Right on,' said Rosie.

'But I'm not sure about ripping things off little shops. Like, if I get wristbands stolen, it's a real drag.'

'Yeah, but the people who were selling this dress, they'd just ripped off the people in Afghanistan,' said Carol. 'So we ripped them off back.'

'But then we should give it back to the people in Afghanistan who got ripped off,' said Rosie.

'Fuck off,' said Carol, with a smile. 'They're not getting

my dress off me, man. No way. And anyway, I don't want to steal things from big stores and banks and places like that because everything they've got is shit.'

We laughed. Rosie tried to get Carol to go into the toilet and put the dress on, but she refused. It was stuffed back into my bag.

When we got back to Hilltop Road, there was a very different mood about the house. Carol opened the door and I could hear a woman's voice I didn't recognize coming from the kitchen. Charlie walked past, looking sneery and making yabba-yabba hand gestures.

'Shit, she's back,' said Carol.

'Hello, Carol dear,' said Gillian, the professor's new wife. She smiled and seemed very pleasant. Her voice reminded me of babysitters who'd looked after me when I was small. A comforting if somewhat loud voice. She kissed Carol on the cheek and looked at me.

'And who's this?' she asked.

'Gillian, this is Rob. Rob, this is my stepmother, Gillian,' said Carol. We shook hands. I smiled.

'Nice to meet you, Rob. Now, Carol,' she said, without a pause for breath, 'can I have a word with you in the kitchen?'

Carol followed Gillian while Rosie and I went into the front room where a large contingent of the North Oxford intelligentsia's offspring were seated around a small fire, looking like they should have been smoking dope. They weren't.

'She's back, man. Totally heavy,' said Charlie.

'She seems all right,' I said, unloading the Afghan dress I'd lugged all the way from the station.

'Wow, where d'you get that?' asked Mike, feeling the cloth.

'Afghan, man,' I said.

176

'Ripped off,' said Rosie. 'From a hip capitalist's shop on the King's Road.'

Charlie held the dress up. 'Far out. Look at all that stitching.'

'Afghan, man,' I said.

'Ethnic,' said Mike. 'Far out and ethnic.'

I laughed, Charlie laughed, Mike laughed a bit, but not as much as me and Charlie. 'Far out and ethnic' became a catch-phrase we would use over and over. At that moment a ten-foot roll of plastic came sailing through the door.

'That's it!' screamed Gillian. 'Whatever this is, you can take it and go.'

'That's Rob's plastic sheet for his geodesic dome,' explained Charlie.

There must have been something in the word geodesic which incensed Gillian. I have often wondered if the word has some sort of unconscious effect on certain people in authority. It did seem to drive large sections of the people I met wild with rage.

'I've had enough,' she shouted, her eyes behind the sixties frames large and determined. 'You can all go now. Bye-bye.'

Charlie picked his cloak off the floor. 'Not you, Charlie. You're staying to clear up this pigsty. The rest of you can go, and take your ruddy plastic sheet with you.'

The motley crew in the front room slowly climbed to their feet. They seemed to know the score; it was inevitable: you just crashed at someone's house until their parents freaked out, then you moved on. There was nothing you could do about it. To avoid this confrontation we would have had to try and behave as they wanted. This was not possible: the gulf between what we wanted out of life and what they wanted us to do was too wide. We were at the tail end of the generation who had really torn away from their families in a big way: changed too much for them to tolerate, rejected too much of what they thought was good and right. We could only stay in their houses in the hope that they wouldn't notice us. There was no way we could live there.

'Where you goin', man?' asked Mike. He was helping me carry my huge roll of stolen plastic.

'I don't know,' I said. Cabbage was trotting along beside me, looking interested in the outside world. 'I might hang this between a couple of trees and sleep out.'

'You can stay at my place for a bit if you want. My parents are cool.'

'Yeah,' I said, hugely relieved inside. 'Yeah, may as well, if that's okay.'

'Hey, man. I've got sounds, dope, joss sticks, vegetarian food. It'll be fantastic.'

Mike and I carried the ten foot roll of plastic sheeting right across Oxford, all the way up the Banbury Road, nearly to the roundabout on the A40, then turned off down a bushy side road and into a very large North Oxford house. We dumped the plastic roll down beside the Volvo in the two-car garage and entered the house by the kitchen door. In a utility room off the kitchen there were two chest freezers, one full of frozen vegetarian food. The other was full of frozen dog meat, for the two pedigree poodles belonging to Mike's mother. No one seemed to be at home.

We entered the kitchen and the two poodles ran away, terrified of Cabbage, who promptly ate all their food, which had been carefully put on plates bearing their names on a mat on the floor. We made some massive sandwiches with far too much inside them: honey, smooth peanut butter, beetroot, cheese in big chunks, lettuce, cucumber and tomato with tomato sauce and real mayonnaise. We drank milk, about a pint and a half each. We didn't speak during this time, just chewed and looked around, breathing noisily through our noses. Mike fiddled with his mother's kitchen things, a picture of a dog, a small bunch of flowers in a bright little vase. He flicked and knocked at these things as he chewed. There was a board hanging near the massive fridge where you could write things with a felt-tip pen and wipe them off afterwards. It had the word REMEMBER printed along the top. This board seemed to annoy Mike, as he kept hitting it. I could hear him saying the word remember through his sandwich. I took a massive mouthful of sandwich and picked up a mauve felt-tip pen from the jar beside the board. I wrote in big capital letters, TO FUCK RIGHT OFF.

Mike choked on his sandwich and sent a fountain of half-chewed food across the kitchen floor. I followed suit, and we writhed about on the kitchen floor in agony, laughing so much our eyes went red, getting up, pointing at the sign and then rolling back down, unable to breathe. Cabbage was busy eating everything that fell out of our mouths.

We left the kitchen, and the board, and went into the entrance hall, which was grander than I'd expect in a suburban house, the stairs rising in three flights, with big heavy wooden banisters, and slightly too big for the size of the house. On the wall at the foot of the stairs was a huge painting of Mike's father, a ten foot high painting, the biggest single thing in the house. He was the director of one of the biggest international charities in the country, and the painting showed him standing in a moody dark interior with one hand resting on a globe. He was wearing a suit, with one hand on the world. Did he care about it or did he own it? I wasn't sure.

'Fascist,' said Mike as we climbed the stairs.

Mike had the attic. It had always been a dream of mine to live in my parents' attic in a big house in a city. They lived in the country in a small house with an attic that was only five feet high.

Mike's attic was painted black and red with loads of posters of bands and weird science fiction landscapes done by the same bloke who did the Yes album covers and, in one corner, a picture of a naked woman lying asleep on a bed with a bit of tangled sheet covering her pubic hair. The picture was soft-focus arty porn, her arms and legs were spread, and you could easily see that gorgeous tendon on the inside of her thigh, and her breasts, and her neck and everything. There was a title in small print along the bottom of the picture: 'Aftermath'.

Mike had a huge ashtray on the floor, full of dog ends and joints, so apparently his parents didn't mind him smoking. Brilliant. He had a huge Bang & Olufsen stereo with four massive speakers, one in each corner of the room, and a double bed.

'Far out and ethnic,' I said, looking around the room.

'Let's skin up,' said Mike, enthusiastically. 'I'm getting almost weirded out by being this straight. I might drop a tab of acid tonight.'

'Dark they were and golden-eyed,' I said.

'Wow, heavy,' said Mike, 'What does that mean?'

'I was hitching in Germany a few years back, and I got a lift in a camper van with two aliens.'

'Oh wow, man! Too much!'

'Yeah, it was far out.'

'And ethnic.'

'Yeah, they could drive without touching any of the controls, they were just so in tune with the machinery. When they turned around to look at me, they could just, like, turn their heads right round. Dark they were and golden-eyed.'

Mike actually stopped rolling his joint and stared at me, his mouth open.

'Fantastic! Did they take you into their ship, you know, like, a flying saucer?'

'Well . . .' I started, my mind filling with images from behind the broken dam of my unconscious, but his phone rang and cut me short. Mike had a phone, a red phone with buttons instead of a dial. He spoke briefly, put the phone down and said, 'That was Carol, she's coming round.'

'Must be heavy at Hilltop.'

'Yeah,' said Mike. 'Did you know I used to go out with Carol?'

I didn't, and it clearly showed. 'Yeah,' said Mike. 'But she dumped me for Mark. You know, weird Mark, and then she dumped him for you.'

'Yeah,' I said, not feeling too confident of my position with Carol all of a sudden.

'Still, it's cool now,' said Mike. 'Sure, I was cut up about it when she dumped me because that Carol is one beautiful chick.'

'Yeah, she's a fine lady,' I said.

'Lay lady lay, lay upon my big brass bed,' sang Mike.

'Yeah.'

'Still, it's cool now. I'm over it, man. I go out with Sarah and we fuck like rabbits. So it's cool.'

Sarah was one of the quiet women. I'd never actually spoken to her, but I knew she thought Charlie and I were immature. She had a bored, deadpan look on her face when she listened to us going on about geodesic domes and cartoon books. I had heard Mike and her having sex, and something about the quietness around her did make her very attractive. I flashed through half a dozen girl-swapping fantasies as we lay around, smoking dope and waiting for Carol. When she arrived, Mike went to make some tea, Carol and I ripped each other's clothes off, kissed with wide-open, longing mouths and fucked each other in a hectic and passionate way, unlike we had ever done before. I felt three years older afterwards. I felt grown-up. We said nothing about Charlie, or her step-mother, or anything, we just fucked and licked and sucked and bit our way into each other's hearts.

Mike returned with the tea and we drank it, ate biscuits, smoked dope and fell asleep. It was a brilliant evening: no worries anywhere, in a North Oxford attic, safe from the streets and the cold and the Vietnam war raging on the other side of the world. The Cold War was at its height, a crook was in the White House and a bunch of bad-suited no-hopers were hobbling around Number 10. But we were safe, in the big bed of the son of the director of a large charity. A man who had himself portrayed in a painting standing next to a globe with his hand resting on it. A bad painting at that.

A week later Charlie and I stood in our new house, smoking roll-ups and feeling quietly excited.

'This is a great little place,' I said. 'Just perfect.' The house, on Wingfield Street, was a little charmer. Think of Coronation Street and you've got it: a narrow, cobbled dead-end street of little red brick, two-up, two-down houses, a shop on the corner.

'Far out and ethnic,' said Charlie. We had squatted the house, using far more subterfuge than was needed. Charlie, dressed all in black, decided to break into the house through the back, which involved a late-night climb right over the house and down the rear wall. It was very amusing to watch, but we discovered the front window was open and so it wasn't an essential operation.

The street was being knocked down to build an old people's home. We were confused by this because the whole street was full of old people who were having to move out. We even spoke to our neighbour, a woman in her late seventies. We assured her that we were responsible young men and had no intention of robbing her in the night. She thought it was a shame they were knocking down the street, and we agreed with her.

Charlie had started making leather things with the offcuts of my wristbands, which in turn were made from the offcuts of David's bags and belts. Charlie refused to follow tradition and used only a pair of nail scissors to work the leather, shunning my growing collection of tools. He made little leather purses, sewn together with soft leather thongs. He managed to plait together little leather buttons, in elaborate Celtic knot styles, which he used to fasten them. They sold like hot cakes in a shop called Turl Trend, on the Turl. I sold my wristbands there since David had sort of given me the wristband concession in that shop. I sold maybe ten or fifteen wristbands a week there. The man in Turl Trend, who had permed Afro hair and wore red clogs, told Charlie that he could sell as many of the little purses as we could make. Charlie seemed pleased, but as soon as anything he did became successful he got bored with it. Carol was more remote, doing her O levels and revising every night.

The period we spent living in Wingfield Street was very calm, peaceful and regular. It was like living away from home should be. We were both working, occasionally Charlie read a school textbook and disappeared for an afternoon to do an exam, and it was easy to imagine we were two responsible, creative and beneficial members of society. I wasn't signing on, I was earning my own living. True, the concept of tax and national insurance payments was well beyond my abilities, and I broke the law by smoking dope, but essentially we didn't do anything wrong.

On the weekends the house would fill up with Charlie's friends from school, Mike and Sarah would come around with cake they'd liberated from his parents, and Rosie would come around with her depression at how fucked up her parents were. We'd sit in the small front room which smelt of leather, and we'd drink tea and milk, eat cake and get peacefully stoned.

The weather was turning, the evenings were long and sunny. After a hard day's plaiting leather wristbands, I'd walk along Wingfield Street's quiet cobbles to the corner shop, an old English corner shop without much stock, and I'd buy ten No. 10s, the cheapest cigarettes on the market. Charlie and I would smoke them in about an hour. They were revolting, but somehow just right. We'd sit and drink tea in our lovely little house. It was the first house I'd lived in since I left home which I felt at home in, felt I could make a mark in and call it mine.

Then one day we came back to the house after a shopping expedition and the house didn't have a roof. It was that sudden. The builders must have waited for us to go out and then ripped the tiles off. I had a lump in my throat as I looked up; it seemed so cruel.

It's hard to say if they had broken the law when they ripped our roof off. We were apparently legally entitled to stay there, which is why no one had kicked us out. The builders wanted to get on and knock the whole street down and build a series of serviced little apartments for pensioners. It wasn't as if they were knocking it down to build a motorway or an arms factory, so we didn't have much of a moral leg to stand on.

We spent two more nights in the house, ignoring the fact that there was no roof, but a light shower one afternoon put paid to that bit of avoidance. Water came streaming in everywhere. We had to take action, and fast.

Carol came around, then we put everything we could into the driest corner of the front room and walked off into the rain. Stepmother Gillian was in high dudgeon and in no mood for midnight visitors, but Rosie's parents were away at a conference so we could go there.

They lived on the Woodstock Road, miles up the Woodstock Road, but we couldn't catch a bus because that meant waiting, and waiting for a bus was straight and boring. By the time we got to the house we were soaked through. However, this was a top-class large family home, with book-lined rooms, modern paintings everywhere, big desks with low lamps, big bathrooms and huge piles of fluffy towels. Rosie was a wonderful host, feeding us, washing up and making beds up.

We were sitting in the kitchen when the first big crack of thunder hit. The lights flickered, Carol clung to me, Cabbage went quivery and sat on my feet, whimpering. I love thunderstorms and wanted to go and look for lightning.

'This is it, man. The start of the big freeze,' said Charlie.

'What's that, Charlie?' asked Rosie.

'Don't you know about the big freeze?' said Charlie enthusiastically. 'Oh wow, it's fantastic! Right, all the pollution, all the cars and trucks and planes, right, they're chucking out all this pollution which is building up in the upper atmosphere, forming like a huge cloud over the whole planet, right. You can't see it, it's just there, right. So, these scientists say, really proper kosher scientists in

America, they say that over the next few years the temperature's going to drop, only by, like, three or four degrees, but that's enough to start another Ice Age.'

'Oh, God. So we're all going to freeze to death?' said Rosie.

'It's going to be really heavy,' I said. 'I always knew it would. That's what all these wars are about. People are going to be fighting and killing each other, blaming each other, when if we just all stopped, you know, really stopped, and saw what we were doing to each other. It's got to be possible to live together without all that shit. Wars, competitive sport, violence, all the heavy stuff. But I guess we've got to go through the nightmare, like the North Vietnamese, you know. I always knew, man, even at school, years ago, I knew that all this shit would come to an end. It has to. There's just too much of everything. That's why I want to get out of it. You know, move out of the rat race, as far as possible.'

'Yeah, Canada, man,' said Charlie. 'The Rockies, too much.'

'Drop City,' I said. 'That's in the Rockies or somewhere. That's why I want to build my dome, find another way to live, you know, so people think, hey, all right, there is an alternative.'

'D'you really think that'll happen, Charlie?' Carol asked seriously.

'What, Robbie's dome, man? Sure it'll happen,' said Charlie, laughing.

'No, the end of the world and all that heavy shit.' Carol looked very worried.

'Yeah, makes sense, doesn't it?' said Charlie without looking at her.

A monster crack of thunder that sounded like it was splitting the house in two made us all jump. Carol started sobbing softly; Rosie put her arm around her. 'Come on, Carol. We've got to be brave. You know, it's, like, a privilege, to see the end of the world. Think of all the millions of people who've lived and died and that was all there was to it. We're actually going to see the end. Cheer up.'

It was a chilling moment, which can only be looked at with comfort from this period of global warming. In the early 1970s it was all global freezing, the big freeze. The end of the world would come when we were all covered in ice. There had been hundreds of articles in the press, television documentaries and books about it.

I wanted it to happen, the sooner the better. The total collapse of the world order as it stood then was the only thing that would satisfy me. I knew it was so corrupt, over built, heavily laden with deadly weaponry, uselessly cruel and hypocritical that it must collapse in on itself like a cancerous corpse. I would walk through the bitter wreckage of the world I'd been born into in grim-faced vindication. I was right; all those teachers and parents and newsreaders with their smug smiles were wrong.

Carol and I lay on the sofa bed in the large rear study. Lightning occasionally flashed on the ceiling. Stevie Wonder's 'Living for the City' was playing on the stereo. It was lump-in-the-throat time for two doomed lovers. Two young people who had been placed on the planet to witness its final demise. Carol held me tightly all night, with Cabbage sleeping right by my head, still twitching as the storm blew away.

The next morning was bright and clear and sunny. Birds sang, the air smelled sweet: it was gorgeous. I went out into the back garden and took my shirt off. I was so white and thin: this was the first sunlight my torso had been exposed to for over a year. It was a wonderful feeling.

Charlie was already out. He was sleeping in the attic so

he had probably climbed down the front of the house and gone off. Rosie shouted out of the kitchen window that there was a phone call for me. It was Charlie: he'd found somewhere for me to build my dome!

Just around the corner from our sodden little house in Wingfield Street is St Clements, a short busy road with a few pubs, a few shops, a bit of a park down by the river, but nothing much to speak of. Just the wrong side of the river for the university to be interested in. One of the houses on St Clements was a squat, and Charlie knew a girl called Emma who lived there. There was no room in the house, but it had a large garden with a fair-sized shed at the end.

'Hey, Emma, man,' said Charlie as we sat in her sunny room overlooking the street, 'can we, like, build a geodesic dome in the back garden and, like, live in the shed?'

'Hey, far out, guys,' said Emma, who then attempted to play a tune on her tiny clay ocarina, one of those annoying hand-made whistle things that no one has ever managed to get a tune from. 'Yeah, a dome in the back would be cool.'

I could see Emma fancied Charlie, but Charlie seemed oblivious to her forwardness, or maybe he just chose not to notice. We all went out into the garden, which was walled and surprisingly spacious for a house so near the centre of town. Hardly overlooked by other houses and very quiet, it was a delightful place, an overgrown orchard basically, with three mature apple trees, long grass, no rubbish and a rambling old brick shed down one side. We found a spot which would be ideal for a platform for the dome and Charlie investigated the old shed.

It was agreed we would move in that afternoon. In the meantime, I set off with Cabbage to start the process of building the big dome. At last, it was finally going to happen. I managed to find Mike in a pub off the High where the more mature members of the North Oxford crowd would congregate – that is, the people over sixteen. He was sitting with Sarah and seemed pleased to see me.

'I've finally got a site for my dome,' I said. Mike stood up and hugged me.

'Far out, man. My mum's been giving me loads of hassle about the roll of plastic. They want to give it to the Third World, man.'

'Well, let's go and get it.'

We caught a bus up to his parents' house in North Oxford. This time there was a brilliant quiche in the fridge, which we finished in seconds, and while we were eating it, Mike tried to explain to Sarah about my previous visit, writing 'fuck off' on the remember board.

'Sorry?' said Sarah, in her posh accent. She clearly didn't understand.

'Like, Rob wrote "to fuck off" on the board,' said Mike, seeming not to pick up on her lack of interest, 'so it read, "Remember to fuck off". It was so funny, man, we nearly choked to death.'

Sarah raised her eyebrows a little and sighed. Mike was a little bit drunk. He started to kiss Sarah, she didn't seem to mind and, without any explanation, they both left the kitchen and went into one of the downstairs rooms. I stayed in the kitchen raiding the fridge and giving Cabbage copious amounts of dog food from the box on the top shelf. I heard a noise from the front room, a grunt and a small female sigh. I moved slowly, opened the door and crept across the front hall. It's an irresistible thing to want to watch. Well, I found it irresistible. I'd never seen anybody doing it before. I could hear the constant rhythm of their lovemaking, a creaking sofa and heavy breathing. I moved closer to the door and there they were, all too clearly, on a sofa which faced the door, with only a coffee table between me and them. Sarah's long, lean body was splayed underneath Mike's large, humping form. They both had all their clothes on, but peeled to the extremities of their bodies, which was somehow a very erotic sight. I don't think they saw me because they didn't hesitate. I moved across the hall and into the downstairs toilet where I masturbated in three seconds flat. It was a pleasant, secret little moment.

It can have been only minutes later that Mike helped me carry the long roll of plastic all the way back down the Banbury Road, unable to catch the bus because the driver wouldn't let us on. We stopped off at Gary and Helen's house on the way and had a cup of tea. Cabbage was very pleased to see them and ran upstairs to what used to be my room and jumped on Gary and Helen's bed and went to sleep. I borrowed a twelve-pound sledge hammer and a wrecking bar from Gary. I had big plans.

'I'm building my dome at last,' I said. 'In the back of a squat in St Clements.'

'After all this time,' said Gary with a kind grin, 'you're going to live in a fucking dome. I don't believe it. Wait till I tell Roger.'

'It's going to be massive, man.'

'Yeah, it's going to be a huge orgasmatron,' said Mike, and for the last time in front of Gary and Helen, I felt slightly embarrassed.

I kissed baby Daisy, who had grown noticeably, and set off down Walton Street and across town towards the future. While I had been engaged in plastic-sheet trans-portation and perving off on Mike and Sarah having sex, Charlie had set about doing up his shed and by the time I got back he had cleaned it out, whitewashed the walls and more or less moved in.

'I'm the fucking hobbit, man,' said Charlie sitting cross-legged on the small shed's threshold. 'Look, I live in a little cottage.'

'Brilliant,' said Mike. 'Utterly fucking brilliant.'

I went back to our old house in Wingfield Street, which you could virtually see from the back garden of St Clements, armed with Gary's tools. There were other builders around, knocking down the far end of the street and filling huge skips with rubble, but no one seemed to mind my presence. I can't imagine what they thought when they saw a long-haired, scrawny youth walking along the street, dragging a sledge hammer and a wrecking bar, and wearing a green-striped pointy hat with a bell on the end. I smashed in the front door of our old house, which they had nailed up to stop more squatters, I suppose. Once inside I started pulling up floor boards, ripping down walls and salvaging as much wood as I could. I worked like a man possessed. I *was* a man possessed. I could see this dome looming up over me, just like the pictures in *We are Everywhere*. It was going to be like the pictures in *The Shelter Book*, where more or less everyone said that one thing all domes have in common is that they leak.

On one return journey to the house, carrying a massive pile of dirty wood along the street, Carol caught up with me and kissed me on the cheek.

'Fucking hell, Rob!' she said, smiling and glittering like a hippie angel. 'What the fuck is all this wood for? Are you building the dome?'

I nodded, turned the corner into the garden and manoeuvred through the narrow gateway. Carol then saw that I had amassed a huge pile of timber. 'Oh, fuck me!' she said. 'How big is this thing going to be?'

'Massive. Absolutely massive.'

Charlie was still looking out of the window of his shed,

smoking furiously. Carol was entranced. 'Charlie, is that your house?'

'Far out, isn't it?'

'It's brilliant,' she said gleefully and looked inside. Then, with a serious note in her voice, she said, 'Oh, wow. It's really nice, Charlie.'

She was looking inside a barely swept-out, concrete-floored, unlined brick shed with a bed supported on six tea chests, a few other boxes and hippie trinkets, a chest with the words Boom Shanka written on it and a slightly ripped African bedspread, dating from the family's year in Ghana when the professor had taught there.

'It's Nirvana, man,' said Charlie, smiling calmly.

Carol went off and bought us fish and chips, Mike went off and bought us beer, which I didn't drink, Coke, which I didn't drink, and a huge pile of cigarettes, which I smoked. Charlie and I started to dig holes to hold the posts which would support the deck, the deck on which we would construct the dome, but the darkness got the better of us.

'Dark they were and golden-eyed,' said Charlie.

'Yeah, heavy. Have to finish the whole thing tomorrow,' I said, throwing down the spade and realizing I was a physically broken wreck. I had taken the minimum exercise possible for the previous two years, I had smoked as much as I possibly could, eaten virtually nothing and slept in sporadic bursts in various unhealthy beds. I had then suddenly had a day of frenetic and very exhausting activity which would have left even a fit athlete a little frayed, and I wondered why I could barely see.

We sat around on the wood and ate chips, smoked and drank beer, Coke and, in my case, cold water from the garden tap.

'This is it,' I said. 'This is what it's all about, being free, not living in houses, building your own dwelling, you know, and just, like, well, *being.*'

'Yeah, hanging out with people who are really important to you,' said Mike.

'Yeah, man,' I said, realizing that he'd just said something important. 'That's right.'

'Welcome to Nirvana Hotel,' said Charlie.

'Far out,' said Mike.

'And ethnic,' said Carol, Charlie and I. We sat in silence listening to the distant rumble of traffic, the static babble of someone's television playing the news, the last few birds of a spring evening as the sun slowly set. The light played across the tops of the old apple trees. It was a magical and special moment.

Carol explained that Gillian was away for the week, the professor was in America, Hilltop was empty. Mike had arranged to go and see Sarah, Charlie wanted to try out sleeping in his new shed, so Carol, Cabbage and I went back to Hilltop Road for baths, sex and sleep.

The long walk up the hill was an exquisite sensation, being so dirty and tired, so utterly exhausted and filthy, but knowing that I was heading for a clean house with a big bath and lots of clean towels, then a big bed with a beautiful girl who wanted me there. I glowed, I definitely glowed that night.

'I love you, Rob,' said Carol, after bathing.

'I love you too,' I said, as we kissed.

'Listen,' she said. 'Listen, if I went to America to see my mum, would you stop loving me?'

This did come out of the blue. I had got used to seeing Carol. Since she had done all her exams, she had been more relaxed and a lot nicer to be with.

'Look, I'd love you whatever happened,' I said. 'You're

the most beautiful girl in the whole universe. I'd wait for ever for you.'

We kissed some more. Carol was reassured but I was feeling uneasy. 'Where is your mum?' I asked.

'Alamogordo, New Mexico.'

'Amazing. How would you get there?'

'I'd fly. My dad said he'd pay for me. I haven't seen my mum since I was six. I need to talk to her again. This is the only chance I'll get of going. I should go, shouldn't I, Rob?'

'Of course,' I said. 'Of course you should.' A pause, then: 'When will you go?'

'July.'

'Shit, man, That's soon. How long for?'

'Three months, or it's not worth it.'

'Three months!'

'It's such a long way.'

'Sure. Sure.' Another long pause. I could see myself being that single man again. Lying in a bed alone at night dreaming of women's bodies. So much time alone. Then I thought of Sarah, of how maybe one day she and I would be on a couch, or in my dome, making love in that different way. Not like me and Carol, sort of dirtier in a strange, sexy way I had no language for.

'Sure,' I said, stroking Carol's hair. 'You've got to go. I'll wait for you. In my dome. I'll be waiting.'

11

Zen and the Art of Geodesic Dome Building

The dome was twelve feet high at its highest point. Really, in all honesty, it looked like a nicely shaped pile of firewood and plastic sheeting. The platform it rested on was quite impressive, however: solid timber uprights sunk well into the soil, bolted to floor joist cross members, then salvaged tongue-and-groove boarding, fitted together and nailed in place. It sat three feet off the ground, a 'low-impact dwelling unit', as Charlie named it. The dome structure was made up of a mixture of badly split lengths of floor joist, half sawn, half axed to length, a mass of splinters, bent nails and traces of my blood. When I had run out of wood with only two-thirds of the dome standing, I hadn't let this dampen my spirits. I resorted to using a few pieces of heavy bamboo pole we had found in Rosie's parents' back garden, a clothes-line prop from Mike's parents' back garden, and most of what we thought was an unwanted flower trellis from the back garden at Hilltop Road. I never personally witnessed Gillian's rage when she discovered that her much loved rose trellis was part of Carol's dippy boyfriend's geodesic dome, but I'm sure it did nothing for her life expectancy.

These disparate lengths of timber were sawn and hacked to the requisite length, drilled using a hand drill with a blunt bit, and then wired together. They weren't just wired together in a haphazard way, they were mathematically joined, five at a time around cut-off pieces of plastic drainpipe, actually bought from a DIY shop for £3.99.

Mike, Sarah, Carol and Rosie sat, smoked and watched

with barely concealed hysterics as Charlie and I moved around feverishly twisting bits of wire, threading them through slices of grey plastic pipe, and then holding them up in back-breaking positions. Their mirth momentarily turned to admiration when we finally started to lift the great wobbling structure off the ground. It lurched from side to side as we added more and more layers of triangles.

'This is going to be amazing, man,' said Charlie, his mouth full of short pieces of wire we had ripped out of the Wingfield Street house and snipped to length.

'It'll change the fucking world,' I said.

'It's going to look like something off a Strawbs album cover,' said Mike.

'I hate the Strawbs,' said Rosie. 'So boring, all those riffs. So boring.'

'The Strawbs are fantastic,' said Mike.

'Rubbish,' said Rosie.

'Who d'you like then?'

'The Stones,' said Rosie.

I started doing my Mick Jagger impersonation, strutting up and down the platform, holding a pair of pliers as a microphone.

'I met a gin-soaked bar room queen in Memphuuuurs, ba be da!'

'You really, really look like him,' said Rosie.

'I think he looks like the drummer from Santana,' said Carol.

'The Stones are crap,' said Mike. 'In two years' time, no one will know who the fuck the Rolling Stones are. They're finished. The Strawbs are just going to be around for ever, man. They're contemporary.'

'Captain Beefheart,' said Charlie.

'Frank Zappa,' I said.

'Janis,' said Carol.

'Yeah, Janis has to be the queen of the lot of them,' I said, Janis now having a very special place in my heart, having lost my virginity with her in my ears.

'When you've got nothing, you've got nothing to lose,' I sang badly.

'Stick to doing Mick Jagger,' said Rosie.

'Janis Joplin's dead,' said Mike. 'Doesn't count if they've killed themselves.'

'She was killed by the CIA,' I said. 'She knew too much.'

We continued naming bands and singers as we fitted the final cut-off drainpipe to the last spars. The structure actually stood up – twelve feet high, twenty-four feet across – and due to the shape of the dome, you could stand up in almost all of it. I wandered around in its magical frame. A geodesic dome, big enough to live in, up on a deck, off the ground, although the deck was not as high as I wanted. I had dreamed it would be ten or fifteen feet up in the air so that you entered by a hatch in the floor. The dome wasn't quite as big as I wanted either: I had dreamed of a sixty or seventy foot ceiling height. Next one, I thought, as we started to unroll the plastic sheet.

One of the important aspects of this dwelling construction was the fact that the measuring and planning were really not cool. Charlie and I had built this whole thing by eye: we didn't have a tape measure, we didn't even have a six-inch ruler. The spars were as long as our arms out-stretched, about six foot. This wasn't a problem since the very nature of the structure compensated for any minor discrepancy. It was almost as if Professor Buckminster Fuller had known that people like Charlie and me would be building domes in back gardens from Builth Wells to Baltimore.

We hadn't, of course, measured the plastic sheet.

'It's not going to be big enough, man,' said Mike as we unrolled it.

'Don't be so negative, man,' said Charlie. 'I can't handle negative vibes. It will be big enough if we believe it is big enough.'

We clearly didn't believe anything like hard enough. The plastic sheet covered about half the dome. It was a disaster. I was close to tears as I pulled and stretched the heavy plastic sheeting.

'Don't worry, man,' said Charlie. He was sitting in the centre of the dome, rolling a joint. He lit it, took a couple of tokes and handed it to me. He pointed up to the high spars and said, through a strained, smoke-filled throat, 'Cover half the dome in clear plastic, the other half in black plastic, so the sun, like, doesn't always come in the dome.'

'Oh wow, fantastic, Charlie! That would look amazing,' said Rosie taking the joint from me.

'Yeah, but I haven't got any black plastic,' I said.

'Rubbish bags, man,' said Charlie. 'Thousands of them, taped together.'

'They've got them in the supermarket,' said Carol. 'We could rip some off.'

'Fantastic!' said Mike. 'Ripping off rubbish bags – no one will suspect.'

'The perfect crime,' I said.

'Teenagers get high on crime,' said Charlie.

'Far out and ethnic,' said the whole lot of us.

We managed to steal a lot of black rubbish bags from a supermarket, but we spent so much money buying soft drinks and cake as a decoy that we would have been better off buying the bags in the first place. Rosie and Carol went off separately and bought some heavy sticky tape, or maybe they stole it as well. By nightfall, the dome was covered in a mixture of clear and black plastic, and we were all sitting inside, drinking milk and eating cake.

'Battenberg,' said Charlie, with his mouth full. 'Oh yeah, that reminds me. I've got to go to court in the morning.'

'Heavy shit,' said Mike.

Carol decided to stay with me that night, to christen the dome. However, Cabbage wasn't at all sure about sleeping in the dome, and Carol didn't want to christen it by having sex since she was nervous that people could see in – which, of course, they could. I was very nervous about everything, hearing sounds that seemed to be just the other side of the thin plastic wall. It was too much like camping in a tent, something I'd never been crazy about.

We did finally get to sleep and the following morning accompanied Charlie to the magistrates' court where we were greeted by the professor.

'Thank God you're wearing shoes, Charlie,' he said as he ushered us inside the grand old building. 'This is Hector. He's representing you.' Charlie shook hands with a very impressive-looking barrister with close-cropped curly hair. Charlie and Hector retired to a corner of the court waiting room while Carol and I sat with her father.

'So how's the leatherwork business then, Rob?' he asked in a kindly fashion.

'Good, thanks,' I said. 'And we've just completed my geodesic dome. We stayed in it last night.'

'Good grief,' said the professor with a smile. 'You've built something and it's still standing. Top marks.'

'It's fantastic, Dad,' said Carol. 'It's huge, it's just amazing, like being in this huge globe. Charlie and Rob worked all day yesterday, non-stop.'

'Worked non-stop all day. That's got to be a first for Charles. Well done for motivating him, Rob. Well, listen, best if you don't come in the court, chaps.' The professor checked his watch. 'You might frighten the magistrate.' He laughed. 'I've got a very busy day but I'll stay and hear what goes on. Bit of an open-and-shut case, I think. Hector will rip the police's case to shreds in a few minutes. He's marvellous. Used to be a student of mine. Top-flight barrister now, very rich man. Poor old police force don't stand a chance.'

He was right. Within about fifteen minutes of entering the court Charlie came walking out, head in the air. 'Hey, man, no case. The police blew it, no search warrant.'

Hector and the professor shook hands and they both left with brisk good-byes. Charlie, Carol and I walked back down the large staircase to the street, passing, as we went, the police drug squad who eyed us with unconcealed hatred. The man who searched me outside the St Bernards Road squat jabbed his finger at me and made a very ugly, tight-lipped face. I shrugged and smiled and kept moving. Charlie, however, decided to have a word.

'Bad luck, chaps,' he said with a big grin. 'Still, better luck next time, and oh, by the way, try and obey the law, eh? You know, the law. Remember that? The thing you're supposed to be upholding. Bye.'

Charlie waved over his shoulder and we walked briskly down the remaining stairs. I felt at the time that this was not a good move. The drug squad in Oxford had an ugly reputation. There was one senior policeman who, rumour had it, was a little on the twisted side since a disgruntled druggie had spiked his doorstep milk with LSD and his children were very badly affected.

Back at the St Clements dome, there were people in the garden, one of whom was Emma.

'Far out dome,' she said. 'These cats live in the house.' She introduced us to a very neat Singaporean man called

Michael, and Stephen, his quiet English lover. They seemed nice but were into Guru Maharaji. Michael and Stephen lived in the tidy basement of the house with little pictures of the Guru on the wall. Ian, another member of the household, clearly not into Guru Maharaji, was a heavy-looking, sweaty-browed hippie who stood with two young women staring at my dome in total bewilderment.

'What's it for?' asked one of them.

'It's a low-impact dwelling unit, man,' said Charlie.

'It's to live in,' I said, desperate for them to understand. 'You see, I want to challenge the rigid structures of straight society with a, like, different lifestyle. We don't all have to live in square houses and have jobs and everything.'

The two women just stared at my dome and said nothing. Emma smiled. I shrugged.

'Hope it doesn't rain,' said Ian, beckoning the two women who obediently followed him into the house.

'He's, like, totally focused on sex,' Emma explained once he'd gone. 'If he's with a woman, he's, like, erect, you know. He, like, knows no other way to relate to women. It's terrible, so it, like, takes two chicks to keep him calm.'

'You mean, those women . . .?' I started asking.

'They're both nurses, over at the Radcliffe,' said Emma. 'They come here whenever they get time off, and fuck Ian until he can't walk. I guess it's a mutual arrangement and everybody's happy.'

'Far out,' said Charlie.

Carol sneered. 'I could see he was totally fucked up,' she said.

I set up my meagre leather-working tools and started plaiting wristbands. Charlie was busy doing something in his shed. I felt good, looking out of the small doorway we'd cut in the plastic sheeting at the surrounding orchard. Carol clearly didn't feel so benign. She was bored and started to complain, reminding me of my younger sister on a bad day.

'Look,' I said. 'I've got to make some wristbands. Dave and I are going to London on Friday to sell stuff, and I've only got a few done.'

'I know. I know. It's just so boring. All you ever do is work. I just want to have a good time. I'm going to America soon. Can't you work when I've gone?'

'But I'm broke, Carol,' I said, pleadingly and not at all attractively. 'What am I supposed to do? My parents don't give me any money. I don't want to sign on. I've got to work, man. That's all there is to it.'

'What am I supposed to do?' asked Carol.

'I don't fucking know. If I knew the answer to that I'd be a millionaire. Be happy,' I said.

'I'm going out, then. See you.' Carol walked out without kissing me. Cabbage looked up from her bed, a little concerned.

That night Charlie and I had fish and chips from the chippie down the street, drank a bottle of beer between us and Charlie smoked a corn-cob pipe which he had stolen from someone's parents' house.

'It's really difficult with chicks sometimes,' I said, knowing it was hard for Charlie to talk about Carol.

'They should all be barefoot and pregnant, chained to the kitchen sink,' said Charlie with a sly grin. 'That's what women really want, to be treated bad by real he-men.'

'Yeah,' I said, half-heartedly. 'Look, I feel bad about Carol, you know, not having anything to do when I work. But man, I've got £3 in my pocket, I've got no savings, no food, I don't own anything except this.' I pointed to the dome.

'When you've got nothing, you've got nothing to lose,' said Charlie.

'Yeah, that used to feel good. You know, maybe I just want to be hitching across America.'

'Do it, man,' said Charlie. 'Peculiar travel suggestions are dancing lessons from God.'

'Wow. Amazing. Is that some sort of Zen Buddhist thing?'

'No, Kurt Vonnegut,' said Charlie matter-of-factly.

'Yeah, just travelling for ever on those endless highways.'

'All highways have an end, man,' said Charlie.

I went to bed feeling depressed. My dome seemed pointless. All that effort, all that night-time planning, drawing, talking, hassling, stealing, carrying and building. All for what? To be able to sleep in a glorified plastic bag. Cabbage cuddled up to me and I dropped into a fitful sleep.

I was roused very late by hissed whispering and Cabbage's tail wagging. I didn't move, I knew it was Carol but I wanted her to think I was asleep.

'He's asleep, man. It's cool.' It was Mike's voice. I could hear he was drunk.

'Look, just be quiet,' whispered Carol. I couldn't tell if she was drunk; she sounded like she was about to burst out laughing.

'Yeah, okay. But you be quiet too,' whispered Mike.

'You're the one who makes a noise,' hissed Carol.

'I won't make any noise. Come here.'

I felt them both get into my bed beside me. There was a lot of thumping which it would have been very hard to sleep through actually, but I kept up the act. After about a minute I realized there was a rhythmic bumping going on: a definite rhythmic bumping was beginning to make the dome sway. Carol and Mike were having sex. They were actually at it, right next to me. They had forgotten all promises to be quiet, lost in the grinding desire. I started to smell their beer-soaked, smoke-stained breath as the pounding got harder and harder. I thought about the energy we use when we have sex: it really is a superhuman effort. The deck started to judder, it occurred to me that my construction skills were not up to this sort of pro-longed hammering, when suddenly Mike grunted, 'Oh, God. Oh, my fucking God,' and with five or six monu-mental humps, the dome settled back to silence.

There was a delicious pause while they listened to see if I was awake. I was biting my lip, holding in the hysterical laughter. For some reason, instead of being upset that my girlfriend had just had sex with her ex-boyfriend in my bed, I found it touching and peculiarly comical. It was clear that they had met at the pub, Mike had done a 'there'll never be anyone like you Carol' routine and it had worked. They'd not been able to go back to his house or Carol's, for some reason, so they thought, where can we go? Mike had presumably said, let's go and fuck inside Rob's dome, and Carol had said, yes, that's a good idea, and that's what they did.

I burst out laughing.

'Oh, sorry, Rob. Sorry,' said Carol.

'Yeah, sorry, man,' said Mike. 'We sort of couldn't help it.'

'It's brilliant,' I said. 'Far out and ethnic.'

Carol was really nice to me after that. I suppose I knew she would be, this being the only logical reason behind my gracious attitude to her behaviour. There was some-thing uniquely harmless about Mike and Carol having sex, in fact I quite liked the idea. Nothing was wrong, except that her departure for America was looming. It hung like a shadow over everything.

The weather held good and clear for about four days and nights. The nights in the dome were great when you could see the stars, but on the fifth day the heavens opened and dumped on us. The dome leaked like a badly fitted baby's nappy. Everything I owned was soaked within minutes. Cabbage sat on a damp blanket and shivered. My bed was so wet you could squeeze water out of the old, flea-bitten interior-sprung mattress. Plaited wristbands sat in puddles and leached their dye into the boards. It was a miserable disaster. I sat in Charlie's shed feeling about as glum as you can, but his shed wasn't much better since the old roof had long since passed its water-proof days. Drips fell all about us for hours.

'Bummer, man,' said Charlie.

'Yeah,' I said.

After a few hours pointlessly waiting for the rain to stop, we went into the house. Emma made us some tea and we dried out. I looked out of the back window at my dome, glistening in the early evening rain. It was hopeless. Without spending a lot of money on wood and paint and waterproofing, insulation, a stove, a door, I wasn't going to be able to live in it. I didn't have a lot of money, I didn't really have anything.

'Listen,' said Emma. 'Gracie, the chick who lives in the front room, she's, like, spaced out and about to move out, man. You can move in there if you want. Not now but, like, next week, when she gets her trip together. She's into Guru Maharaji, and they think, like, the world is going to end.'

'When's it going to end?' asked Charlie enthusiastically.

'Next weekend, I think,' said Emma. She played a dull

note on her ocarina. 'All the Guru Maharaji people are going to some place in Crystal Palace, like, in the park, and they're going to meditate together, leave the earth, you know, levitate. They're going to go, like, collective astral travelling, and leave the whole world to destroy itself.'

'Brilliant!' said Charlie.

'So she doesn't want her room then,' I said, ''cause she thinks we'll all be dead?'

'Yeah, man. The chick's fucked up,' said Emma. I had a quick peek inside her room. It was plain, white, almost empty except for a small bed and a picture of the little fat boy who had at the time an absurdly large following. Guru Maharaji was big money in 1973.

'You can sleep in the top room tonight,' said Emma. We climbed the stairs behind her. On one of the hall walls was a full-size advertisement poster for Lamb's Navy Rum. It was the woman in the wet suit with the zip half undone so you can just see the sides of her breasts. It was huge: her teeth were the size of your face as you walked past.

'That was already up there,' said Emma. 'Sexist crap.'

I nodded in agreement, looking at the poster and imagining Carol in a similar outfit. We entered the top room. It was very nice, with just carpet on the floor and the two very low tiny windows facing the street and one very large one at the side of the house.

'No one lives in here,' said Emma. 'This is like, our communal room, you know, where we can all get together and get stoned and that. People might drop in late at night for some blow, that's all.'

'That's cool,' I said. With the state I felt my life was in, people could drop in for some blow all night.

It would have been about three in the morning. Charlie was wrapped in an African bedspread and I was fast asleep with Carol when the door smashed open and a body fell on the floor.

'I am out of my fucking brains,' said the body. 'Pilled up to the eyeballs. Totally smashed out of my tiny fucking skull, man.'

'Heavy,' said Charlie.

'Hi, man. Sorry,' said the figure as he scrambled to his feet, only to topple over again with a bone-crunching thud. 'Wow,' he said, rolling around on the floor, 'Drugs can really soften the world, man. Everything is soft. Wow. Hi, everybody. I'm Rick.'

Charlie got up and switched the light on. 'Hey, man. Are you all right?'

I could now make out that Rick was wearing a cheap leather jacket, torn jeans, and a dirty T-shirt. A mop of dirty hair fell over his pale face.

'Yeah, man. I'm so fine. Utterly fucked, man, but cool. Yeah.' His yeah was loud and long and mad. It caught you by the scruff of the neck and said, 'Come on, let's go out and have fun.'

We introduced ourselves. Rick pointed to himself and said, 'I'm Rickorius Dementius.' He then pointed at us, one by one, with an unsteady hand. 'You're Roberto Royale, you're Charlius Chalkus and you, sexy lady with the dark eyes, are Carolius Resin.'

We laughed. We had been woken at three in the morning. We had just met Rickorius Dementius. The man who would change all our lives.

12

Storming Magdalene

Since building a geodesic dome which leaked, which had soaked my meagre possessions and, with the first bit of serious wind, had collapsed in a heap of ripped plastic and damp wood, my hunger for self-built dwelling units had diminished somewhat. It's hard to describe the emotional acrobatics I experienced, after the months of thought, dreams and struggle to build this magnificent structure. At any rate, I was desperate to move into a house after four short days and nights of dome habitation. Thankfully Gracie, the odd Guru Maharaji follower who lived in the big front room at St Clements, went to Crystal Palace to meditate, thus allowing me to move in as a resident of the house.

A week after moving in, I was standing on Magdalene Bridge at midnight, wearing a full-length black crêpe dress with a high round collar and puff sleeves, ready to crash a college ball. I was in a group of about fifteen variously dressed long-hairs, all trying to look smart. Rick and Charlie were there, both wearing black dinner suits, white shirt and tie.

The clothes had appeared in the afternoon when Rick arrived with a big black bin-liner stuffed to bursting with stolen goods. There had been a squabble over who was going to wear what, and there was a point when it didn't look like I was going. Rick hadn't stolen enough and got in a temper, until someone suggested I wear the long black dress. This was originally stolen for Carol, but she refused to go.

'Crashing balls is really stupid,' she'd said. She was going to stay in my room, alone except for Cabbage. We had spent the whole evening getting ready. Ian's two nurses had done my make-up and hair, a tousled top-knot with two curls either side of my face.

'Fuck me, you're a woman,' said Rick as I posed in front of a full-length mirror. He looked puzzled for a moment, then said, 'D'you shave your armpits, man?'

Carol laughed. 'He hasn't got any hair there.'

'Late developer,' I said.

'Have you got any balls?' Rick asked flatly.

'Yeah, of course,' I said, rather offended.

'Has he?' Rick asked Carol. She nodded with a smile. I smiled. It was a brilliant moment. It was something to do with being accepted by an older man, a rude, loud, cheap, thieving, dangerous, drug-abusing older man, but none the less, he accepted me, protected me even. There was nothing really happening, but the evening sun coming through the windows, the dress feeling different around my body, Cabbage lying sleeping on her rug, Carol's beautiful smiling face and the sheer burning energy of Rick's presence made the moment stay with me.

'It's the hands that give it away,' said one of the nurses. 'Keep your hands behind your back and no one will know.'

I looked into the mirror we had propped up against the old fireplace.

'Jean Shrimpton,' said one of the nurses.

'Yeah, that's who he looks like, Jean Shrimpton,' said the other. Everyone agreed that I looked like Jean Shrimpton. I had no idea who they were talking about, but I have since seen pictures and, providing you half close your eyes, in the dusk, just taking a quick glance, there was a fleeting resemblance.

We used socks inside one of Carol's bras so that I just had small breasts, not some huge joke, man-in-a-dress breasts. I looked like a woman. As I stood on the bridge in the cool air, I even felt like one, demure, eyelash-fluttering and sort of bendy in the lower back. We could hear the music coming from within the high walls.

'There's no way we can get in,' I said. 'It's got walls all around it.'

'Listen,' said Rick, looking surprisingly respectable. 'Pirate Paul's nicked a boat, and me and Charlie have got a grappling hook and a load of rope. We go over the river, man. They're not guarding that wall.' He pointed up to the ramparts of Magdalene, at least forty feet above the water.

'Oh, fuck!' I said. 'I've got to climb up there, above that?' I looked down at the water from the bridge. I couldn't swim. I had no excuse. I'd never been to a school without a swimming pool, I'd never met another kid who couldn't swim, I'd been taught by the best and the worst, I'd been helped in a sensitive way by kind, caring teachers, I'd been thrown in the deep end by vicious schoolboys. Nothing worked: I was terrified of water. Nice clean water in a swimming pool was bad enough, the horrors of a murky brown river at night cannot be expressed in words, only screams of panic.

Beyond the walls of Magdalene, far up the river, there was some movement. Pirate Paul appeared from underneath overhanging branches, giving rise to a small cheer from our crowd who were leaning over the parapet of the old bridge. Pirate was a solidly built man with black hair, wearing the regulation black suit and bow tie, and with a wicked seafarer's grin. He waved at us to come down, all the time checking the ramparts for the enemy. Following Rick, who ran at a crouch like a commando on a raid, we went down the Magdalene boat ramp at the side of the bridge, where students and tourists hire punts. The ramp was unguarded as there's no direct entrance to the college that way. So far we had seen no sign of guards or any other kind of security people.

When we reached the water the low rhythm of music was louder; my heart was thumping, reaching a panicky crescendo as I stepped into the leaky punt that Pirate Paul was trying to keep stable. More people piled in, laughing quietly and rocking the boat violently.

'Don't fuck about now. I can't swim,' said Pirate Paul. I was thrilled at this news.

'Nor can I,' I said smiling.

'Yeah, so watch out, the young lady doesn't want to get all wet in her lovely dress,' said Pirate, his soft West Country burr giving away his ancestry. Charlie and Rick laughed.

'It's a bloke,' said Rick. 'It's Roberto Royale. He's a bloke.'

'Fuck me!' said Pirate. 'I was thinking about shagging it later.'

'Charming,' I said.

'All right, everybody ready, here we go,' said Pirate, pushing the punt out into the river. We had to travel only twenty-five yards to get to a part of the wall which wasn't so high and was away from the road and the street lights. This short distance seemed to take ages, with everybody speaking in hushed voices, looking up at the ramparts to see if any security guards had seen us.

'If they spot us now, we're fucked,' said Charlie. He looked like a member of the French Resistance, the long coil of rope over his shoulders, the big grappling hook in his hand, his hair pushed up inside a beret. The fact that any of us thought we would blend into a ball being attended by the future élite of the nation only shows the power drugs can have over those parts of the brain which judge reality.

'This is it,' said Charlie. 'Rick and I came down the other day, stood on the bank over there.' Charlie pointed into the blackness of the trees on the opposite bank of the river. 'This is the lowest part of the wall. The other side is gardens which don't look like they're being used. If you get over the wall and run to your left, down the stone stairs, you get into the quad under the tower. That'll be packed with people, you can suss it out once you're in there. If security catch you, smile and do what they say. They can get quite heavy.'

'Any of them puts a hand on me I'll nut the fucker,' said Pirate Paul.

'Okay, everyone get down. Charlie's got to do his swinging the grappling iron trick,' said Rick. 'He nearly took my fucking head off this afternoon when he was practising.'

'Hey, man. It's cool,' said Charlie, who already had the hook swinging from his right hand. We squashed down as best we could and Charlie started to wind the heavy three-pronged grappling hook around his head. The wind whistled as it built up momentum. He let fly and I lost sight of it as it sailed into the night. There was a silence, followed by a splash.

'Shit,' said Charlie. 'A bit short.'

'G'iss it here,' said Pirate Paul. 'I'll get the fucker over.' Paul pulled in the rope from Charlie, and the boat nearly went over. I screamed. Ian held me around the waist.

'Don't worry, pretty lady, I'll save you,' he said, winking at me. It felt weird, but nice, to be looked after by a tall man. I worried momentarily if Ian's problems with women and erections would be transferred to me now I looked like one. But there was nothing obvious poking me in the back.

Pirate Paul started swinging the rope with such violence I felt sure the boat was going to go over. The hook took off into the night with an audible hiss like a wire-guided missile. It flew over the top of the wall, thirty feet above our heads, and made a dull clunk somewhere the other side.

'There you go,' said Paul, pulling the rope tight. 'Probably gone over to Cornmarket.' We all laughed. He was referring to Oxford's premier shopping street, at least three-quarters of a mile from where we were.

'Probably hooked on the front door of Woollies, man,' said Rick. There was more hysterical laughter, everyone seeing the image clearly.

'Yeah, probably some cop looking at the rope stretched up over the roof and thinking, duuh, where's that from?' I said, doing a dumb cop routine. No one laughed, I pushed some hair out of my eye and swallowed.

'Now, who's first?' said Pirate Paul.

'I am, man. I'm a cat burglar. I'll be up there in five seconds,' said Rick. Three minutes later Rick was on the top of the wall after struggling and swearing, hanging precariously off the rope and looking like he was destined to fall in the river all the way up. Charlie followed and really did make it up the rope in no time. Ian followed, being very fit. All that sex clearly was a good training. Then it was my turn.

Being six foot tall and weighing eight stone had its advantages. Your body weight is so small in comparison to the length of your limbs that heaving yourself up a rope should, according to mathematics, be quite easily accomplished. But I was a weakling, a wet wimp, scared of water and wearing a full-length black evening dress which should have been on some student at the ball. It took me all the strength I could find, both emotionally and physically, to climb that rope. I have to admit the last five feet were managed only because Pirate Paul climbed up the rope behind, a terrifying enough experience, and pushed me from below with a strength that felt mechanical, not human. When I stood up on the parapet, it was all worth it: the lights were bright, the music loud, the people a whirling mass of colour and energy. It was a magical moment, the smell of a summer evening, smoke from outdoor cooking, a living dream, a fairy ball in a mythical castle. These were lucky people, they knew it and were having a ball. A wonderful May ball.

'It's brilliant,' I whispered to Charlie.

'Biggest ball there is,' he said. 'They have one only every three years. They have really big name bands, free food till you can't walk. Cake to dive into, man.'

'Far out.'

'Free champagne, gallons of it.'

'Free chicks, man, begging for it,' said Rick as he passed.

Five more people struggled up the rope and on to the wall. We were forming quite a little crowd and clearly had to disperse. By the time I followed Charlie along the wall and down some stone steps there would still have been a few left in the boat. It was every man for himself by this time. Rick, Ian and Paul were in front of us, running at a crouch and laughing all the time but we didn't follow them. Charlie vaulted over the rail and on to a roof. I followed, glad I had opted for the black Tai Chi shoes as opposed to some very high-heeled ladies boots which I had tried on and could just about cram my feet into. I watched with delight as Charlie lifted a lead hatch cover set on to the roof. A beam of electric light made his long face stand out oddly against the night sky. We looked inside: a long corridor with paintings on the walls; there was no one about. Charlie dropped in: it looked like quite a fall, but after the climb up the rope, this was easy. I followed, trying as best I could not to catch my frock. I landed with barely a sound on the floor. This was *The Man from UNCLE*: Charlie was Napoleon Solo and I was Ilya Kuryakin, I had to wear the frock as a disguise so that Thrush agents wouldn't recognize me. We both looked up at the open hatch. There was no way we could get back up and close it.

'Hope it doesn't rain,' I said.

'Fuck it, man,' said Charlie. 'This is too easy.'

We walked down the corridor together as quietly as we could, then froze as a door opened on our right and two old men with grey hair and evening dress stepped out laughing.

'Evening sir, evening madam,' said one of them, a kindly twinkle in his eye. I smiled back, just showing him my teeth. He was delighted. 'Have a lovely evening,' he said.

'We will,' said Charlie. 'We will.'

We went down a flight of polished wooden stairs and into a quadrangle. The noise was amazing, the shouts of thousands of the most confident people on earth, music, champagne corks popping, screams of laughter and smiling faces everywhere. I lost Charlie in seconds, wandering through the packed throngs of dark suits and long dresses. No one seemed to pay me special attention, though I noticed the odd glance from a young man as he looked over his partner's shoulder. I always smiled slightly in response.

I found a table laden with so much food it was impossible to see where to start. Hundreds of people were picking at it, filling their plates to overflowing. I saw a queue and joined it. A couple in front of me were snogging wildly and staring into each other's eyes with such rapturous intensity I was transfixed. They broke off their kissing, noticing my stare.

'Hello,' said the woman. 'Lovely evening.'

'Yeah,' I said. 'It's beautiful.' Their faces froze for a moment's hesitation when they heard my voice, rather deep for a pretty young girl. I quickly put my hands behind my back and stared into the milling throng.

'Haven't we met?' said the man. I smiled, vaguely recognizing him, but shook my head. He ate toast at Brasenose. I shook my head some more, and his girlfriend pulled his arm.

'Gareth, you're embarrassing her,' she said. They returned to their snogging and I breathed a sigh of relief. As we moved slowly forward I had time to look around. High up on the walls surrounding the beautiful gardens stood men in dark clothes, armed with big torches. Each one of them had a large badge pinned to his lapel; some of them were in black suits with bowler hats. They were the security guards; the ones in bowler hats were the élite bulldogs. They were standing watching the rich and influential have an amazingly good time, prepared to cause injury to anyone who tried to join them without paying for it. I looked around for my compatriots, who were nowhere to be seen.

I reached the head of the queue and was handed a plate by someone I recognized. His thin long hair hung dankly either side of his odd, pointed-featured, shiny face.

'Gollum,' I said.

'Evening,' he said with a sly grin. 'Have we met?'

'It's me, Rob, Rob the leather worker. I go out with Carol, Charlie's sister.'

'My, you have changed,' he said quietly.

'Are you working here then, man?' I asked.

'Keep it down, old son,' said Gollum. 'Had a security guard on my tail a moment ago. This seemed like a good idea.'

'Brilliant,' I said. 'Good luck.'

I moved along the table and managed to cram a massive pile of food on to my plate: chicken, ham, pork, turkey, beef, lamb cutlets, beetroot, cheese, potato salad, rice salad, pasta salad, Greek salad, prawns, sauce, mayonnaise, bread, more potato salad, more beetroot, a sudden find, that chunky cut-up Russian salad, masses of that, more turkey, a massive slice of quiche, mushroom salad, another chunk of bread, this time with cheese and a huge dollop of pickle.

I carried my heavy plate around the quadrangle looking for somewhere to hide and eat, and I saw Ian and Rick talking to three very attractive women, smoking a joint. They looked happy. The women laughed and stared up at Ian and Rick eagerly. I realized then that it was doubtful that any women would stare up at me eagerly, unless they were lesbians, and I didn't know much about them. I thought of Carol, sitting in my room the other side of the river, stroking Cabbage in the peace and quiet. She would be going to America soon and I wasn't spending time with her. I was standing in a quadrangle of Magdalene College, with a plate piled high with stolen food, wearing a long black dress.

Then I saw Duncan. Duncan, the small-mouthed homosexual from Brasenose who had given me the garlicky snog. I hesitated for a moment, but it was just too tempting not to show off. I walked towards him.

'Duncan,' I said softly, close to his ear. He was talking to a very tall man with dark hair and a big nose. Duncan turned, looked at me with a fixed smile but no recognition, then, before I could say anything, his face opened in magnificent, fulfilling amazement.

'Oh, my God!' he said. 'Oh, my God. Robbie, is it you?'

I laughed and Duncan embraced me far too violently.

'Duncan, who is this delightful creature?' said the tall man, with the plummiest accent I have ever heard. His Adam's apple bobbed up and down in a cartoon-like parody of a chinless wonder. It sounded affected but looked natural.

'This,' said Duncan, holding the tall man by the sleeve to steady himself, 'is Robbie, he's a boy, Gerald. Robbie is a boy.'

'Oh, come on, Duncan. You're pissed.'

'He used to work in the kitchens at Brasenose. He was an angel, a Fellini angel, grubbing about in the dirt. Oh God, then one day he just flew away. Broke my heart.' Duncan looked at me with a slushy, drunken grin. 'Robbie, tell him you're a boy, won't you?'

'Yes, I am,' I said and shook his hand. 'Nice to meet you, Gerald. I'm looking for somewhere to eat, I'm starving.'

'This is so extraordinary,' said Duncan. 'A boy in a long black frock. This is a very special night.'

'Calm down, Duncan, for pity's sake,' said Gerald, whose speech sounded ever more affected to me. I laughed aloud.

'What's so funny?' asked Duncan.

'I don't know. I'm so hungry, I've got to eat. Where can we go?'

'Eat here,' said Duncan and fell on the grass with his arms raised and his glass of champagne flying over some unfortunate people nearby. 'It doesn't matter tonight. Tonight nothing matters.' I joined him, sitting awkwardly on the floor, with my legs to one side, as women sit; it's extremely uncomfortable if you're not used to it.

'What have you got underneath there?' asked Duncan grabbing crudely at my frock. I pushed his hand away.

'Nothing,' I said through a massive mouthful.

'Nothing!' said Duncan, his head in his hands. 'Gerald, he's got nothing on under the frock. Oh, my God. Let's make love.'

'Please,' I said. 'I'm having my tea.'

'Tea,' screamed Duncan. 'She's so rough. Tea. I love it. This is rich. This is so rich.' He grabbed a bottle of champagne from Gerald, who was now talking to someone else with his extraordinary voice. Duncan poured a glass and offered it to me.

'So, what have you been doing with yourself, Robbie?' he asked.

'I live in a commune over the river. It's called Nirvana Hotel. I've built a massive geodesic dome in the back garden. I'm making leather stuff, wristbands, belts, pouches, stuff like that. You can see it in Turl Trend on Turl Street. I'm starting up a comic, you know, cartoon magazine with this guy I've met. I'm living with a chick who's dad is a proctor of the university. I go to London all the time to sell leather stuff. I'm having a fantastic time.'

'You live with a chick!' he exclaimed.

'Yeah. I'm straight, Duncan,' I said. I didn't feel in the mood to go through the rigmarole again.

'How can you say that when you look like this?'

'It's just so I could get in here.'

'Oh, I see. I think,' said Duncan. He emptied the champagne glass which I had failed to drink, re-filled it and offered it back to me. 'So who brought you here?'

'Pirate Paul. We came in over the back wall, next to the river.'

'You gatecrashed!' said Duncan, slightly too loudly for comfort.

'Yes, threw a rope over the wall with a grappling hook on it. Sort of like a Commando raid. My best mate was in the Commandos, and another guy was in the SAS, so if the security people touch them, there's going to be some dead bodies to clear up in the morning.'

'How glorious!' said Duncan.

'Could get really heavy,' I said, enjoying myself. 'We've been training for weeks, it's like a political act, you know, to crash the balls and get wrecked, steal stuff, well, liberate it.'

Duncan sat looking at me, frozen in a state I didn't recognize. I couldn't tell if he was horrified or close to orgasm. Quite possibly he was both. He flopped back on the lawn, spilling champagne. 'I always fall in love with the wrong boys,' he wailed, then he sat back up and held my shoulders. 'I don't see you for years and then you appear out of the crowd in a long black dress. Is it surprising? Then you tell me you've gatecrashed, gatecrashed the Magdalene ball. This is the best ball ever, Robbie.'

'I know. How's your book?' I asked, still busy eating.

'I've got a publisher. He was at All Souls, left a couple of years ago. I knew him from school.'

'Eton,' I said.

'Yes, that's right, Robbie. Well remembered. Anyway, they've got one of their chaps doing the illustrations, I'm afraid. It's due out in November.'

I was half way through explaining how I only wanted to do political cartoons anyway when Duncan disappeared as two young men in dinner suits landed on top of him. For a moment I panicked, thinking they were security guards who had meant to get me. Then they both shouted, 'Duncan!' at the top of their voices and rolled about on the grass together. My champagne went flying, but I managed to save my food and stood up.

Duncan struggled to his feet. 'Robbie, don't go,' he said, another man's arm around his neck. 'Please, let me have one kiss.'

The men stood up either side of Duncan and straightened their clothes, looking at me. The one on his left raised his eyebrows. 'What's happening, Duncan, old chap?'

'It's a boy, you fool,' said Duncan quite snappily. 'This is Robbie.'

'Oh glory, glory Hallelujah,' said the other man.

'Please, Robbie,' said Duncan. 'Just one kiss, that's all. For old time's sake.'

'All right,' I said, knowing there were no old times but quite liking to create an impression that there were in front of our small audience. I took a swig of Duncan's champagne, swilled it around my mouth to wash the food down, embraced him and kissed him on the lips. He held me tight and we kissed for a long time. I didn't mind; somehow it was right, I was saying good-bye to Duncan and Tom of Finland. Even though I was in a dress, a period of confusion was left behind.

A cheer of delight went up around us. It seemed hundreds of drunk, scruffy young men in dishevelled evening suits were standing around watching. As I broke the kiss and stood back, Duncan was swamped by jubilant friends. I waved to him beneath the pile, and he reached out for me as I walked away through the crowds. I turned away from the noisy throng and saw Ian being pulled along by two very big, burly-looking guards. He was relaxed, eating and smiling as he was frogmarched towards the exit.

'Gatecrasher,' said a man standing next to me. 'Hope they give him a good seeing to. I didn't pay ninety-odd pounds to mix with the riff raff.'

I gulped at the price. They had paid more money to be

there than I'd earned in the last six months. Ninety pounds to stand around and talk, which is what the vast majority of the people seemed to be doing. There did seem to be endless free food and free drink, but £90! I saw Charlie in the distance, standing with a group of students, talking earnestly.

'Charlie,' I said from behind him. 'The tickets cost ninety quid!'

'Yeah, be cool, man. Security have sussed we're in here. They're on the look out. They've got Ian. I don't know about Pirate or any of the others. I just saw Rick legging it down the other way.'

'We should move,' I said.

'I'm cool here for a bit. These guys are my dad's students. I can blend with them, man. They're cool. We're going into the music area as soon as this guy has put some joints together. Go in, man, under that arch. It's really packed. Fanny are playing in a bit.'

I walked as gracefully as I could through the crowds, keeping to the middle of the quad, where most people were gathered. Two security people stood at the entrance to the music area. I hesitated for a moment, then walked towards them with a smile on my face. They didn't even look at me as I passed straight by them and into another quad with a strange light coming down from above. On second inspection I realized it was a giant geodesic structure, eighty feet above my head, covered in taut white canvas and lit from above. It was beautiful. My heart leapt as I saw it: a massive geodesic dome against the medieval walls of the college. I stood staring up at it smiling. All the effort I went to seemed so paltry when compared to the giant splendour above my head. And this had been built for one night.

At the far end of the quad was a stage where men with

pony-tails and black T-shirts were running about for no apparent reason. Then a scruffy-looking woman appeared behind a microphone. A huge cheer, mixed with jeers and whistles, went up from the packed crowd. I started moving forwards as the woman spoke, something about everyone having a fantastic time, about the fact that we were about to see a brilliant band from the States, so could we please put our hands together for Fanny.

Four women appeared on stage as the crowd roared their greeting. I could only just make them out from my vantage point near the back. They stood around in silence for a while as they plugged in their guitars and adjusted microphones. Eventually one of them said, 'Hello, Oxford' with a broad American accent. The cheer was deafening. The immortal phrase, 'Are you having a good time?' was met with equal fervour. Then the first chord of the first song hit us with such power that I jumped.

Fanny were a brilliant, loud, heavy rock group. I didn't expect them to be like this. For some reason, in my mind's eye they were going to be like the Incredible String Band or the Third Ear Band, weird hippie stringy folky stuff. Not heavy rockers. They even stood with their legs apart and shook their hair like Led Zeppelin and Status Quo. The women played their instruments seriously, looking depressed, dark-eyed and shagged. Brilliant.

'Fantastic!' shouted a voice. It was Mike, grinning and standing right next to me.

'Hi, man,' I said. Mike's smile was frozen. 'It's me,' I said. Suddenly his face popped with amazement. He shook his head wildly and stared again.

'Rob, man, I thought you were a chick,' he shouted above the din of Fanny's speakers. 'I'd moved here, man,' he said laughing, ''cause I saw you, thought you were a single chick. Amazing.' He gave me a hug.

'Yeah, I got dressed up so I could crash the ball, man. How'd you get in?'

'Bought a ticket, man,' said Mike without flinching. 'I had to see Fanny. They're fantastic. Look at the bass player chick. She is so hot, man.'

He was right. I hadn't noticed her before. She was very sexy, with lovely teeth which you could see every now and then when she sang harmony. She wore a thin shirt, tied up, all ripped and ragged, so you could see her smooth belly.

'I'm really sorry about what happened in the dome, man,' shouted Mike into my ear. He had been conspicuous by his absence since the night of the dome's first test coupling.

'It's cool,' I said. 'I'm not into the whole jealousy trip. Just fucks you up. Where've you been though? Haven't seen you in ages.'

'A levels, man. Been studying. Total bummer, but I want to come here, you know, study, rave on all night and shag loads of top chicks.' He was bouncing up and down, clearly on a type of drug I had yet to try. 'I'm going to meet the bass player. I've left a note with their stage manager. D'you think she'll shag me?'

'She's bound to, man,' I said. 'All the chicks want to shag you, Mike.'

'Yeah, right, man,' said Mike, who then shook his mass of hair like Roger Daltrey during a Keith Moon drum break.

I eased away from Mike's manic dancing and moved to one side of the crowd. I saw an open door, leading on to a stone corridor and into another stone-floored quadrangle spread with hundreds of candlelit tables. It was a glorious scene, with people sitting around talking, waiters moving through the crowd with trays laden with champagne and beer glasses, the clear night sky above. To one side, gentle chamber music was sliding out of a well-lit room. I could see people dancing together gently, men in dinner jackets, women in long dresses. I wandered around the table as if I were looking for someone, avoiding people's eyes in case they knew I shouldn't have been there. Suddenly I felt a soft grip on my forearm and prepared for the worst.

'I know you, don't I?' said a voice. I looked down. A woman, with thick dark hair, cut short, and wonderful teeth. I knew the teeth, the smile, but the hair looked unfamiliar. I nodded, trying to remember her face. Then I felt a rush of angry adrenaline course through my heart. It was Margaret, the poetry professor I'd met on New Year's Eve. The woman who had cut me dead over the toast in the Brasenose dining room. My face broke into a broad, happy smile. She was sitting down, I was standing up, she was at a table with another woman and a very peculiar-looking man. I was wearing a long black dress. She knew my face but couldn't place me. It was an exquisite moment, one that, thanks to dope and champagne, I didn't destroy with my mouth. I stood in front of her silently, feeling as sexy as I've ever felt, my shoulders thin and bare in the candlelight, my parts free and loose under the cloth of the frock.

'Who are you?' she asked, smiling broadly.

'I'm Robert,' I said as softly as I could.

'New Year's Eve, at Mary's house,' she said, pointing towards the red-haired woman who I hadn't recognized. 'My goodness, you look different.'

I had already lost interest in Margaret. I was staring at Mary. She was a goddess. She was so beautiful: freckled pale face, narrow green eyes and a thick mop of red hair tied in a loose bun on top of her head.

'Would you like to join us?' said Mary. I smiled and sat down on a vacant chair.

'How are you, Robert?' asked Margaret.

'I'm very well.'

'You look wonderful.'

'Is it a boy?' asked the odd-looking man as he put on a pair of glasses.

'Yes, it is,' I said with a smile.

'My God.'

'I don't normally dress like this,' I said. 'I just wore it for the ball.'

'It suits you,' said Mary. 'You look extraordinary.'

'Thank you,' I said with as wicked a smile as I could manufacture. Mary and Margaret looked at each other. There was something going on here I couldn't keep up with. These women were way out of my league.

'I gatecrashed the ball,' I said, feeling safer talking than being stared at in silence. 'The frock is a great disguise: the security guards haven't even looked at me.'

'You haven't got a ticket!' said Mary. I shook my head and glanced around for mythical security guards.

'That's a bit off, isn't it?' she said, pulling her chin in as she spoke.

'Why?' I asked, noticing a hint of hostility in her voice through the pleasurable haze I was experiencing.

'Because everyone here has had to pay so much for a ticket,' she said with a forced smile. I raised my eyebrows. My blood was up so quickly there was no time to check it.

'Well, they can afford to because they're over-privileged.'

'I remember now,' said Margaret, putting a hand on Mary's forearm. 'He'll get angry about over-privileged students and go very red-faced. He wants to bomb all the colleges and hang the dons from the rafters or something.'

'Goodness me!' said the odd-looking man.

'Don't go red-faced, Robert,' said Margaret. 'It will spoil your make-up.'

'How did you get in then?' asked Mary.

I described the rope and the wall. She smiled. 'You really wanted to be here, didn't you?'

'Seemed like fun,' I said. There was something mean in Mary's eyes and I wanted to goad her. 'Plus it was a challenge. You know, if all these people are having such a good time, and it costs so much, and the college spends so much to keep poor people out, it's like a challenge to break in. You know.'

'Yes, I know,' said Mary. 'It's very interesting.'

I wanted to know why it was very interesting, but I didn't know how to ask. I was getting angry again and it felt wrong. These were the beautiful people and I wanted to be one of them, but they had worked hard at school, they had come from big houses in the country which had entrance halls full of green wellington boots. I didn't. Most annoying of all they knew what they were doing, why they were doing it, and how successful it would be when they'd done it. I didn't. They knew what they wanted to do from when they were ten years old. I didn't have a clue and I was seventeen.

'But if you want to blow up colleges, you think violence is going to help change the world?' asked Mary.

'I don't want to blow anything up. I get angry about things sometimes. You know, hypocrisy, snobbishness, the arms race and stuff. Pollution.'

'He dreams about dogs,' said Margaret.

'Dogs?' said Mary.

'Not every night,' I said, rapidly feeling like I was losing the thread.

'I must say, I'm a little shell shocked,' said the funny-looking man. 'A boy in a dress who wants to blow people up because they're dons.'

'He's a don,' said Mary with a laugh as she put her beautiful hand on the odd-looking man's shoulder. I felt jealous that she had touched him. I felt uncomfortable in their presence. Everyone I had met since I left the urban peasants had agreed with everything I wanted to do. They thought all my ideas were brilliant and that I was brilliant. These women looked like hippies, they looked like they smoked dope and had sex, they were young and incredibly attractive, and yet they clearly found me rather dull. Me, in a frock, with make-up on and a pair of socks stuck down inside my girlfriend's bra. How could they find me dull?

The don looked at me as if I were some sort of slug he'd found on his underpants. I wanted to go but I couldn't leave. I didn't know how to break the silence, which was becoming agonizing for me, though clearly not a problem for Mary and Margaret.

'Is Maurice here?' asked Margaret.

'Haven't seen him,' said Mary.

'You'd like him,' said the don looking at me over the rim of his glasses. 'Well, he'd like you.' He laughed in a high-pitched squeak, which was not very becoming. Mary didn't laugh. I felt my pulse race as I imagined jumping across the table and smashing his nose with a flying head-butt.

'Are you okay?' asked Margaret.

'Um, I have to go. Some security guards have seen me,' I said.

'Come with me,' said Mary, touching my hand. She smiled at me. I stood up; so did she. We went around a large stone pillar and I glanced back at the table. I noticed the don and Margaret talking to each other and laughing. I'd lost all the power I'd felt from wearing the dress. I felt like a hopeless seventeen year old with a powerful infatuation for an older woman. I felt real. Mary took me into a corridor which ran off the quadrangle. A gaggle of evening-dressed people passed us, thundering down some old wooden stairs. Mary leant forward and kissed me on the lips.

'I just wanted you to know that I like you,' said Mary.

'Oh, God. I can't. Yes. I like you too,' I said, stuttering and fumbling. She smiled, held my face and kissed me again.

'It's difficult to explain,' she said. 'You just have to believe me. I can feel something between us but it can't be allowed. D'you understand?'

'Well, I . . . Yes, I suppose I . . .' I was twitching uncontrollably, I just wanted to be languorous and I was behaving like a horse with a gadfly up its arse.

'Be careful,' she said.

'Yes. Okay. I will.'

'Good.' She turned on her heel and walked out of the door. I followed her a little, but somehow I knew I could not go back to the table. I watched her slim waist staying steady as her lovely limbs moved her across the floor. The most beautiful woman I had ever seen, staggeringly beautiful. Strong, disagreeable, powerful, red-haired, annoying, rich, with a beautiful house in Builth Wells. I have never seen her again.

I walked into the room where the dancing was taking place and immediately saw Rick hanging from a woman whose left breast was virtually exposed. I walked up to him.

'Hey, Rick, man, what's the time?' I said. He turned to

me in a massively over-acted drunken lurch, his full weight dragging on my neck as he slumped, smiling, down my dress.

'Roberta, this is Geraldine,' he said, introducing the woman. 'She's a student and I'm in love.'

We shook hands.

'He's a bloke,' said Rick, his face hovering far too close to mine, and his breath stinking of booze and fags.

'Oh, fantastic!' said the girl, in a plummy accent. She was a well-built woman, attractive in a horsy, county, healthy sort of way. 'You crashed the ball too?'

'Yeah.'

'Far out.' She sounded like a member of the royal family.

'D'you like my dress?' I asked.

'It's brilliant,' she said.

'Even I fancy him, and I'm straight,' said Rick. 'I don't fancy him as much as I fancy you though,' he said, planting a huge and obviously rapturously received kiss on Geraldine's lips.

'There's a room we've been using to get stoned in,' said Geraldine. 'There'll be no security guards there, come on.'

'Far out,' said Rick, imitating her accent. He lurched off towards a door in a hectic stumble. Geraldine screamed and grabbed him, dragging him towards another door. They barged into other dancers and waiters as they made their chaotic way out of the room. I followed, still not quite sure what to do.

We arrived at a beautiful wood-beamed and white plaster room in the eaves of one of the buildings which, on second inspection, turned out to be a first-class drug-users' den. Ashtrays with roaches piled high, a mirror with the stain of lines of coke still visible, cigarette packets and bits of card strewn all over. The Robert Crumb cartoon poster, 'Stoned Again', was pinned up on the wall, next to the poster of the girl playing tennis feeling her bum.

Rick collapsed on the bed, struggled with his trousers, undid them, pulled them half down, pulled out a lump of black hash from one pocket and threw it at me.

'Skin one up for me, Roberta,' he said, and then with a slight grunt he nodded his head towards his groin. Geraldine obliged by instantly taking his penis in her mouth, right in front of me, with the light on.

I didn't stare too much. It didn't feel cool. I started hunting around for matches and tobacco as though being in a room with two people having sex was an everyday occurrence for me. I stuck two Rizlas together and imagined if I had been in this room with Mary, and if I'd lifted my dress up and nodded at my penis and grunted. Would she have done the same thing? Try as I might it was impossible to imagine.

As I filled the papers with tobacco, Rick and Geraldine went through the 'struggle to get enough of each other's clothes off to have sex' routine. It seemed to take ages, but very soon they were copulating like two devils. Rapid and violent is the only way to describe Rick's love-making technique. I started to laugh. Rick stopped, looked over at me and smiled.

'Oi! D'you mind? Get on and skin up. I'll be finished in a moment.'

Geraldine pulled his head back to hers and they continued. The door opened and a very tall, slim and quite beautiful woman wearing a light blue dress with stains down the front put her head around the door. She stared at Rick and Geraldine for quite some time, but they paid her no heed, going at it like the proverbial. Then she glanced at me.

'Have you seen Simon?' she asked.

'No, sorry,' I said. 'D'you want to smoke some dope?' I half hoped she'd stay and she and I could do what Rick and Geraldine were doing.

'Too pissed. I'd throw up. Have they seen Simon?' she gestured towards the grunting couple.

'I don't know. Have you seen Simon?' I asked, laughing more and more.

Geraldine's face appeared, flushed and glistening, from beneath Rick.

'Yeah, he's with Sally and that lot in the JCR,' she said. The tall girl nodded and left, closing the door carefully.

'I'm going to come,' said Rick politely and thrashed about a bit. Afterwards I lit up the joint and passed it to him as he struggled to do up his trouser buttons. Geraldine got up and pulled her dress back up without losing her dignity. She seemed very happy, gladly took a toke of the joint and lay back on the bed.

'Better now,' said Rick, looking around the room with a fresh-faced wonder. 'Anything worth nicking, Roberta?'

I shook my head. 'Why so glum, Princess?' he asked.

'Nothing, I'm just knackered.'

'You need stimulants. Let me see what I've got,' said Rick, riffling through his pockets. I shook my head.

'I'm going to bed,' I said. 'I'm fucked off with the whole thing.'

'Oh, please don't go,' said Geraldine. 'I want all my friends to meet you. They'll be here soon with loads of champers.'

'Yeah, man,' said Rick, stretching the word man again. 'Charlie and a load of dudes are on a champagne-hunting expedition. They're going to liberate some, man. It's the revolution, right here, tonight, Roberta.'

We smoked the joint and hung out of the small dormer window, looking down through the trees at the twinkling lights below. I could see Mary and the strange don walking hand in hand towards the dance floor. She was with him; they were probably married. How could she? He was so ugly.

The door burst open behind us and Charlie entered carrying a box. He was followed by a lot of long-hairs, including Gollum and Mike, and immediately I was lost again in the fury of the party. Charlie opened the box. It was full of champagne, and although I had no idea at the time, I realize now that the box would have been worth several hundred pounds. Twelve bottles of very expensive-looking champagne. We more or less had one each.

'D'you get thrown out?' asked Charlie.

'No, I was talking to some people I knew from Brasenose,' I said, 'and some Jungian analysts I used to hang out with.'

'Far out,' said Mike. 'Was that the really amazing-looking chick you were talking to?'

'Yeah, we used to have a thing, but she's married her don. He's a total prick.'

'D'you want him topped?' asked Rick. 'I could have him finished,' he clicked his fingers, 'like that.'

'No man. It's all over anyway.'

'I got thrown out twice,' said Charlie. 'But I just came right back in again.'

'Wow, they threw you out!' I said. 'How d'you get back in?'

'Last time I just went right over the top of those buildings, you know, along the front, right by the gate. They were so busy chucking people out they never noticed.'

'I got chucked out, man,' said Rick. 'Yeah, they threw me right across the fucking road. Drugs softened the blows, man. I just smiled.'

'What, they hit you?' I said incredulously.

'They beat the living shit out of me, man. The way I feel now I reckon they drove over me in a truck. Of course, that could've been Geraldine pounding away on top when I was shafting her.'

'Rick!' screamed Geraldine. 'You're so rude!'

'Yeah, I love you, babe,' he said and started kissing her.

'How d'you get back in though, man?' asked Charlie, who had somehow managed to furnish himself with some wicked-looking chocolate cake. It was in a paper bag in his pocket, mashed, but it still tasted good.

'Geraldine opened a window for me round the back. Inside job, mate. Then I gave her an inside job.'

'Wey-hey,' we all said. I was feeling better. It may have been the champagne but it was also definitely being with people worse than me. More dangerous, more revolutionary in some way, caring less about manners than I did. Sitting with Mary and Margaret and the don had made me so tense. Being with Charlie, Rick and a pile of no-hoper long-hairs, tucked up safely in a small attic room in Magdalene College, was far more conducive to relaxation. I swigged at my heavy champagne bottle and burped loudly.

'Far out,' said Geraldine, who promptly collapsed on the bed.

By the time I made it to the bottom of the stairs, the sun was shining. I wanted to go to bed so badly I couldn't really see. I had a hangover and I hadn't been asleep. There were still hundreds of people milling about, some of them looking decidedly the worse for wear, some looking absurdly clean and tidy. The harsh light of day, however, removed a lot of the magic. The quad lawns were ankle deep in litter, empty bottles, broken glass and cigarette ends.

I found my way through the quad and along a corridor

where I heard the familiar sounds of a kitchen in action. I smiled to myself as I walked past. They were still working, they'd been at it all night. A man with terrible bags under his eyes came out of the kitchen carrying a huge tray of kedgeree. The smell was amazing. I followed him.

He walked into the quad where all the tables had been, the table where I'd sat with Mary. It seemed like another life already. The kedgeree was put next to ten other trays of kedgeree on a long table covered with linen cloths. I sat down and helped myself to a massive plate.

After a dozen mouthfuls, Gollum sat down beside me. We ate in silence until Pirate Paul joined us.

'I fucking love kedgeree,' he said brightly.

We laughed, spitting rice and fish across the floor. I was so hungry and yet feeling so sick that it was hard to know what to do. We drank coffee and smoked cigarettes, by now completely oblivious to the fact that we were gate-crashers and not meant to be there. We watched as people still screamed and laughed and talked around us, no one paying us any attention at all.

'I know a lot of them bouncers,' said Pirate. 'They never chucked me out, man. Knew it wasn't worth the effort. I've been scallywagging all night.'

We nodded in admiration. 'I had to use cunning,' said Gollum.

'I had to use cunnilingus,' I said, which got the desired response. 'Can't wait to get out of this fucking dress,' I said and stood up. I waved and walked towards the archway which felt as if it was the way home. I opened a door on to a large quadrangle and, shielding my burnt-out eyes from the bright sun, recognized the railings which faced the High. There were large tents on the lawn with music, more food, more people. I walked past them and up to the entrance which was busy with people leaving. The bouncers on the door, uniformly thick-necked and ugly, allowed me through without hesitation. Out on the street a large crowd was standing around, for what I don't know. Rolls-Royces and Bentleys, Jaguars and Mercedes lined the street. Once away from the entrance it was deliciously quiet. I looked up at the tower of Magdalene. It was only ten past five.

I walked back towards St Clements, over the bridge. A cheer floated over the river; something was still happening. A large red hot-air balloon floated above the trees. I kept walking and saw a drunk student in a dinner suit being sick over the parapet of Magdalene Bridge. I left him to it. Almost too soon I was back home, in the quiet peace of my room. I slipped off the dress, pulled on a dirty T-shirt and climbed into bed with Carol.

13

Speed Kings

Carol, Cabbage, Rick and I slept in a tent on a National Park cliff top in Cornwall, right next to a sign that said No Camping. The tent was made for two people so it was rather a tight fit. Carol slept in the middle, Cabbage at our feet, and Rick all over the place.

'Wow, man,' he said, long and slow. 'I'm in heaven.' I heard a pill bottle rattle. 'But I'm slipping, man. I'm nearly out of Moggies.' He was referring to his pills, Mogadons, a very powerful depressant. I heard another bottle of pills rattle, and Rick laughed.

'No, it's all right, man. I've got me Mandies. Mad magic Mandy randy madness Carolius Resin.'

Mandies were Mandrax, another clinically developed depressant with a sensual, warming effect.

'Okay, let me see.' Various pill bottles were shaken. 'Uppers, downers, inners, outers, trips, mushrooms, crashers, smackers. Yeah, man. I'm a walking drug store. I've got something of everything, man, we can stay smashed, stoned, ripped, ravaged and bewildered for months, man.'

I had taken a Mandrax, the first time I had ever taken that sort of drug. I lay in a blanket feeling like I had no nerve endings. Everything was comfortable, even the rocks under my back were warm and comforting, and Cabbage's angular body resting on my feet was a soft hot-water bottle. Rick's constant babble was delightful background music.

I got up in the morning when I heard a car pull up beside the tent. Cabbage barked as I emerged, swollen eyes and puffy-tongued into the glare of the bright morning sun.

'Can't you read?' asked the man in the Land Rover. He was official looking but wasn't a policeman. The night before when I had worried about parking there and putting up a tent Rick had suggested we pretend we were French. I stared at his door, which had the word council on it.

'*Quoi?*' I said, scratching my head.

'Read the sign,' said the man, pointing at the No Camping sign we had tied a guy line to. 'No camping. What, are you stupid?'

'*Pardon, je ne comprends pas.*'

'Fucking Frogs. I might have known,' said the man.

''Ello, we leave soon,' I said with as much French accent as I could muster.

'Yes, you leave right away,' said the man, starting his car up and moving off at speed. Cabbage and I watched him disappear up the tree-lined lane, then we turned around together to see a magnificent view of the sea and rocks, waves crashing, sea gulls circling. It was heavenly. I breathed in; my chest hurt, the result of hundreds of cigarettes. Cabbage sat down and sniffed with her head held high. Her eyes half closed, she clearly thought this was pretty good too.

Rick stood up out of the tent, still dressed as he had been the day before. He opened his fly and pissed where he was, right outside the flap of the tent, farted enormously and grinned at me.

'Roberto Royale, you did the French thing, man. Mad magic.'

'*Quoi? Je ne comprends pas,*' I said, and started urinating too, right near the tent. Carol emerged to see what was happening.

'Fucking hell, you guys. Couldn't you go to a bush or something?'

'Bushes are for wankers,' said Rick. 'Roberto Royale and I are marking our territory, like dogs, man.'

Cabbage squatted down and did a piss right beside me, which was very unusual behaviour for her. She normally had a run around and a sniff before her morning wee.

'Hey, far out, man. Look at Cabbage. She's joining in, man. Far out,' said Rick, waggling his penis around in the morning sun.

'Oh, fuck it,' said Carol. She squatted down about a foot from the side of the tent and had a leak herself. We all laughed hard, standing with our genitals exposed, patches of dark urine stain by our feet. The sound of softly crunching gravel warned us that a car was coming down the track towards us. It was a Rover 3 Litre, maroon, with little flag stickers on the side windows.

'Members of the bourgeoisie approach,' I said.

'I wish I was taking a crap, man,' said Rick. He crouched and grimaced, clearly forcing his bowels. He farted loudly. 'No, nothing doing.'

The family in the car were so like my own, quiet respectable people who love the countryside and are members of the National Trust. The sort of family who wear walking boots, carry grey canvas rucksacks with Tupperware boxes full of sandwiches and drink orange squash. They would have been horrified to see three scruffy people, genitals exposed, their dog unleashed, standing on a beautiful grassy promontory overlooking a stunning bay, with a tent up next to a No Camping sign.

The father, who was driving, naturally, turned the car around without stopping and moved smoothly back the way they had come.

'We frightened the living shit out of them, man,' said Rick.

'Yeah, but I bet they'll call the pigs,' said Carol. 'We should get going.'

'Pigs, man! Don't bum me out with pig vibes. Let's split the scene,' said Rick, getting in the car and starting it up with the loose wires which hung below the steering wheel.

'What about the tent?' I asked.

'Leave the fucking tent, man,' said Rick. 'I don't want to meet the pigs, not when I'm carrying so many drugs, man.' He held up a plastic bag, heavy with pill bottles, dope, cigarettes, matches, cigarette papers and a small bottle of whiskey.

I looked out of the back window as Rick thrashed the car up the dusty track. The tent looked tiny and forlorn. We rounded the bend and it disappeared for ever behind the dense woodland. The little tent Rick had stolen the day before, which I quietly coveted.

Everything had changed so quickly. Rick's arrival in the top room at St Clements a few weeks before started a completely different episode in my adolescence. Something which had been holding me back all my life fell away behind me. Manners, morals, learned behaviour, thought before action, fear of consequences, thinking of other people, not being selfish, asking permission, saying sorry – all the things my parents had worked hard to instil in me for fifteen years, rules on how to be a decent human being – all fled in the night.

Rick's energy, his momentum through life, meant these things couldn't keep up. You either had to bail out or drop them, and, like two nights previously, as we sped through west Oxfordshire lanes at midnight in a stolen car, I wasn't about to cling on to them. It was too exciting to miss. I hadn't been in a car for ages, and then only in the back of my parents' car, as part of a normal family. Being in a stolen car is very different. I looked out of the back window, watching the street lights of small villages shrink into the blackness of the night, watching my old life disappear and a new one rush towards me. I could never go back, I'd taken an irrevocable step, a step I'd been longing to take but didn't know how.

Map reading in a stolen car, being driven by a man who only knows one throttle position, fully open, is an exhilarating and terrifying experience. It was so bad, so completely bad and unjustifiable. I wrangled with the evil, the badness and the stupidity of what we were doing, shouting above the noise of the screaming engine.

'The whole system is so messed up,' I said. 'The whole concept of ownership needs to be changed. All property is theft. Therefore, as we don't own this car, we haven't stolen it.'

'Yeah, man. Heavy philosophy,' said Rick, taking a corner at a speed an Austin 1100 was never designed to do.

'We're just using it and relieving the so-called owners of the burden of their theft, their original theft, by claiming to own such a thing. You know.'

'Read the map, Rob,' said Carol. She was lying along the back seat with Cabbage, who by now was visibly pregnant.

Life had taken several turns for the worse since Rick had arrived – faster, harder, funnier turns maybe, turns which cocked a grinning snook at conventional society, which overturned everything that straight society stood for – but everything had got worse. The theft of the car didn't sit comfortably with my ideas about an alternative society, about wind-generated power and geodesic domes.

I was still living in the house at St Clements and carried on making leather wristbands in the front room, but during the day there were more and more people in the room taking more and more drugs. I smoked more and more dope, spending weeks at a time constantly stoned. People descended on the house day and night. Pirate Paul, Big John the cabby, Pete the junkie, Blackfoot Bruce, John Paul Rous, a six foot eight lunatic with massive eyes and wild hair who was always exhorting us to 'get into the castle'. Crazy, drug-abusing hippie nutters who couldn't be trusted and made me feel uneasy.

Pete the junkie, in particular, was very worrying. He was spotlessly clean, his clothes were neat and pressed, he had long hair but it was tied back tight and brushed im-maculately. One day he was sitting on my bed next to Cabbage while I was sewing a leather belt pouch, when he flicked a hypodermic needle with his forefinger, tied a tourniquet around his arm and inserted the needle into a swollen vein. He then sucked blood into the syringe barrel and injected himself with heroin. I found the whole bizarre spectacle sickening, but spectacle is what it was. Junkies want you to watch, they clearly get off on the thrill of shocking people with the gruesome process of getting high. I wouldn't stand for it and thereby got the reputation for being heavy.

'You're really heavy, man, you need to loosen up,' said Blackfoot Bruce, so called because he never wore shoes and his feet had long ago turned the colour of the road.

'No one smacks up in my room,' I said. 'I don't give a fuck what anyone says, I don't want that shit in here.'

'Right,' said Carol.

'You're both really heavy,' said Bruce.

'Fuck off then,' said Carol. I was so proud of her. Bruce

slowly got up on his filthy feet and took his fetid body out of the room.

'I sort of feel bad about this,' I said to Carol. 'You know, being heavy and that.'

'They're horrible,' she said. 'You shouldn't feel sorry for them. They should all just fuck off.'

'I know, but where are they going to go? That's what worries me, man, you know, sweeping problems away just means that there's, like, a bigger problem somewhere else.'

'Yeah, well, let someone else deal with it. I don't want them hanging around here. They're fucking useless.'

There is no point trying to suggest that the St Clements house was a happy commune. We called it a commune: Charlie and I had even gone to the trouble of painting huge flowers all over the exterior walls of the house. You can still see them to this day, crudely overpainted with red brick colour paint.

We had christened the house Nirvana Hotel – the name was also painted in weird lettering next to the front door – and there were periods of time when we felt we had control of what was going on there. But residents from the next-door squat, like Blackfoot Bruce and Ian the perv, meant that the door was open to some of the most unpleasant elements a town like Oxford had to offer. No matter what efforts I made to counteract it, the house was utterly chaotic, filthy, drug-strewn and quite danger-ous. It reached a peak for me, and a turning point in my life, when I came home with a bag of shopping to find my room stinking of drink and dirty men. I walked in to find it was full of street dossers whom Blackfoot Bruce had brought back.

'They're just my mates, man,' he pleaded when he saw my furious face.

'Hey, welcome, brother. Have a drink,' said a decrepit

remnant of a human being lying on my bed. I didn't say anything, I turned and left the room. I went downstairs, put my shopping on the kitchen table, looked around me, saw a broom which was lying on the floor, picked it up, smashed the brush off and returned to my room, armed and ready for action.

'All right, everybody out now,' I shouted as loud as I could. Three or four got up and left immediately, swearing and stumbling, their trousers falling down, shoes dropping off as they went. One of them sat tight on the floor and told me to fuck off. That was all I needed. I brought the broom handle down on his head with an audible whack.

'Too much, man,' said Blackfoot, scurrying out of the room. Another drunk stood up to attack me, swearing and thrashing around in an attempt to look menacing. I stomach-jabbed him with the handle, hard. Much too hard. He folded in two, groaning and writhing. I started kicking the remaining two men as they crawled towards the door. I wanted to kill them, these filthy, lazy, stupid, ignorant, ugly wrecks. I had lost control, I had lost my liberal skin. Any resistance from the drunks was responded to with the most astonishing amount of violence from me.

When we finally got outside one of them picked up a milk bottle as he stumbled down the front steps and lifted it to attack me. He was so slow it was heartbreaking. I side-swiped him around the head with such force that his feet left the ground.

When he landed I noticed there was an extraordinary sound coming from behind him, a throbbing, growling sound so loud and deep it made the concrete step I was standing on vibrate. Two huge motor bikes had pulled up the front path. Rick was a pillion passenger on the first one and he grinned at me insanely as he saw what was going on. The man who'd picked up the milk bottle stood up, blood pouring from his head. I kicked him in the back and he hobbled away. I jabbed him in the back again with the broom handle a few times to keep him going. The motor-bike engines were turned off, leaving my ears ringing with the noise.

'What's happening, man?' asked Rick.

'Blackfoot brought a whole load of alchy bastards back. They were all in my room, they've destroyed it, man. It's a shit hole.' I was still staring at the disgruntled crowd of drunks on the opposite pavement. They were waving semi-clenched fists at me in a pathetic attempt at resistance. I heard one of them shout, 'We'll fucking get you, cunt!' which, instead of chilling me with horrors to come as in the past, fired me up into kill-mode. I charged across the road towards them, traffic honking and skidding as I ignored the danger. The men scattered but I managed to smack a couple of them over the head, jab them and scream obscenities.

I walked back across the road with the broom handle over my shoulder, feeling ten feet tall. I felt older, harder, less happy but not scared. For the first time in my life, I wasn't scared. The two men riding the motor bikes had removed their helmets. One had a beard, the other very long black hair.

'Thierry and Patrice,' said Rick. 'French geezers.'

'*Bonjour,*' I said.

'*Tu parles français?*' asked Thierry.

'No, sorry.'

'You 'ave finished killing the drunk people?' asked Patrice with a smile.

'Bastards,' I said. I turned to Rick. 'Blackfoot has to go, man, before I fucking kill him.'

'Yeah, man,' said Rick. 'It's all really heavy, man.'

Somehow, that afternoon as I cleaned out my room and washed my sheets, Rick bullied Blackfoot Bruce into moving into Charlie's shed, and Charlie happily moved into Blackfoot's pit of filth on the third floor. Not only that, Blackfoot actually knocked on my door and apologized.

'I'm sorry, man. I didn't think. I was only trying to be friendly.'

I felt bad after that. By the evening, the two French motor cyclists, Carol, Charlie and I were sitting drinking tea in what had been the battlefield of my room.

'You've got to take it a bit more easy, Robbie,' said Charlie. 'You can't go round smashing people's heads in with poles.'

'But I just got so angry with them. They're fucking useless. I don't know what it is. I hate violence, but they just shat on my life.'

'I'd have bottled the fuckers,' said Carol.

'One of them tried to bottle me,' I said.

'And you caved the side of his head in, man,' said Rick. 'I couldn't believe me eyes. There's me, I'm hitching back from a big score up the smoke. Thierry and Patrice give me a ride. I tell them I live in this really cool house, like a commune, man. I say, "It's really mellow, man", don't I?'

Thierry and Patrice nodded and smiled.

'We get here and someone's being beaten to death on the doorstep.'

'It was very funny,' said Thierry. 'If those men ever give you more trouble, Patrice and I will sort them out. We 'ave both been in the army.'

Patrice nodded and smiled.

'Wow, heavy,' said Rick.

'Brilliant bikes, man,' said Charlie, sitting on the

246

window-sill looking at the solid black machines parked on the front path.

'Honda 750-4's,' said Rick. 'Race tuned up to Isle of Man TT standard, drop bars, stubby exhaust and goes like shit off a shovel.'

'You can 'ave a ride, Rick,' said Thierry. 'Take the killer with you.'

Within three minutes we were doing a hundred miles an hour up Headington Hill, on the wrong side of the road. I held on to Rick with a bear hug. Every time he changed gear, my helmet slammed into his; I couldn't hold my head steady under such force. I had never moved so fast in my life. We were at the roundabout on the way to London before I could catch my breath, then Rick swung on to the Oxford bypass and let rip. For one eye-watering second I caught sight of the speedometer. We were doing 120 miles an hour, so that cars speeding along at seventy seemed stationary as we overtook them, and frightened the life out of ourselves.

Within a few moments we were at the Banbury Road roundabout, in North Oxford, right near Mike's house. We slowed to a merciful twenty-five as Rick swung the bike round and headed back on to the burn-up dual-carriageway section of the bypass. Cars in the left-hand lane were a blur as we rocketed forward, nothing but open black tarmac in front of us. Then suddenly there was a Morris 1000 van, white, with a sign-writer's name on the side, pulling out in front of us. We were going so fast I didn't even feel Rick falter on the throttle before we slammed into the side of it with an enormous smashing noise. I heard Rick shout in pain, I felt like my kneecap had come off. The bike kept going somehow, although we got dangerously close to the central reservation. Rick seemed to go faster and faster. We climbed up the hill to the roundabout at a mere one hundred and pulled over in a dust-strewn lay-by. It took both of us to pull the bike on to its stand. We inspected the damage.

'We should be dead,' said Rick, hobbling around on the grass verge. His jeans were soaked in blood. 'We should be fucking dead.'

As I moved I realized something was painfully wrong with my leg. I rolled up my flares and saw a nasty gash on my thigh, just above the knee, which felt swollen and watery.

The Morris van pulled up, the driver got out and was very concerned.

'I just didn't see you,' he said. He was a nice old man with white hair. 'I looked in my mirror, nothing, then bang. You surely caved in the side of my van.'

We hobbled around to look. The side of his van was a mess. A deep gouge had been made by one of the pedals, and some lower part of the engine had also come into contact with the van, as we could see by the smear of white paint on the bike. But Rick's leg had taken the brunt of the impact. Badly scarred and bruised, it was extraordinary that he wasn't more seriously injured. As what happened began to sink in slowly, all I could see was a repeat of the accident, with us flying off the bike to a grisly, 120-mile-an-hour meeting of destiny with the road and a concrete post.

When we got back to St Clements, my mother was standing out on the pavement with Charlie and Cabbage. She had dropped in to see how I was.

How I was was limping with my face splattered with Rick's blood. My mother was not well pleased, particularly since my elder brother had been in a very serious motor-bike accident only four years previously. Motor bikes were not a popular mode of transport in my family.

My mother sat in my room at Nirvana Hotel and had a mug of tea, somehow managing to talk and joke with Rick, Charlie and the French motor cyclists. I walked outside with my mum as she left, and just before she got into her car she turned to me. 'I don't want to know what you're up to, my lad,' she said. 'I don't want to know where the bikes came from. All I'm saying is, if you're not very, very careful, you are going to be in big trouble. Very serious trouble.'

'I won't, Mum,' I said. 'I'm not doing anything wrong.' She completely ignored my pleading.

'Just be warned, my lad. Very serious trouble.' She gave me a peck on the cheek and got into her car. I watched her drive away and felt slightly unnerved. My mum was always on my side, always supportive of my plans, very rarely criticizing me. What did she know? Had someone said something to her? Surely not Charlie. As I walked back to the house, I felt unsafe. Was I doing anything really bad? To live outside the law, you must be honest. I was being honest, although stealing wasn't really honest. Anyway, I'd only stolen an Afghan dress from a trendy shop in the King's Road.

It was only days later that Rick pulled up outside the house in the stolen Austin 1100 and took Carol and me on our last holiday together before she left. My mother's words were lost behind a wall of noise and excitement.

The holiday, if you can call it that, was fast, loud, ugly and cheap. It had to be cheap as none of us thought to take much money with us. Anyway, we didn't have any money to take. We got quite far down into Cornwall, when the car ran out of petrol. We somehow hitched back to Plymouth, with no food, nothing to drink, only depressant drugs to take. We had to steal another car in order to get back to Oxford, and we needed one with a full tank.

Somehow, through the haze of drugs and lack of sleep, we ended up in a car park in Plympton, a big car park with loads of cars in it. We crawled around looking for a suitable car. I found an MGB GT, something I'd always wanted a ride in.

'Don't be a thick bastard,' said Rick quietly. 'We'll get spotted a mile off in that thing. Another Austin 1100, man. Piece of piss to steal and no one looks twice at the fucker.'

Carol pointed at a Morris 1100 parked under a tree. We ran towards it, crouched over. If anyone had been watching, we couldn't have looked more suspicious. We sat on the still warm tarmac by the side of the car as Rick slid the window open. Security clearly hadn't been a top priority with the 1100's design team. Once inside, he produced a huge set of car keys on a giant ring. After about five attempts he found one that fitted the ignition. He turned it, the ignition lights came on but it wouldn't turn again and kick the starter motor.

'It's cool, don't panic, anyone,' said Rick. 'Sit here and blip the throttle when I start her up,' he said. He got out of the car and I slid into the driver's seat. He opened the bonnet, pressed something and the starter motor turned the engine. It started straight away, I kept my foot hard down and the engine screamed.

'For fuck's sake,' shouted Rick as he slammed the bonnet. 'What d'you want to do? Wake up the whole of fucking Devon?'

However mad Rick seemed to get, he was always affectionate moments later and we drove back to Oxford without incident. The car ran out of petrol in a back street behind St Clements and we left it there, undamaged but a little worn around the edges. I sat in my room late at night wondering how the car would get back to its owners, and pondering how much they would hate us, what they would think we were like. Terms like 'young hoodlums' and 'sneak thieves' seemed to be most likely. 'Joy riders' didn't have currency then, and we didn't burn the car when we'd finished with it, we just parked it somewhere discreet, trusting the police to find it and return it to its owners.

Carol had one more night in the country before she left. We spent the time in bed, not making love, just sleeping and holding each other. I made her a cup of tea, and as I stood in the kitchen waiting for the kettle to boil, I knew I was going to miss her. I looked up at the ceiling, thinking she was sleeping just the other side and yet in a few days she'd be on the other side of the world. I took the tea upstairs and watched her sleeping face. She was very relaxed and very beautiful. There was no sign of the worry she was apparently feeling about her impending trip.

She left in her dad's car the following morning, and she was crying as they drove away. I went back into the house; there was no one around. Even Cabbage had left, gone off somewhere to scavenge for food. I wasn't feeding her very regularly. I went up to Rick's room. There were eight televisions piled up against one wall, about five stereo systems stacked behind the door and, in the middle of the room in pride of place, a guitar and amplifier. I had never played one before, but spent the next two hours making loud, clanging, electric guitar noises as I waited for the pain of Carol's parting to subside.

I was sleeping heavily one night thanks to some pills Rick had given me, when I was awoken by a great deal of noise outside the house. It came from a beaten up single-decker bus, painted with flowers and tantric symbols. A man with long blond rat's-taily hair jumped out of the driver's cab and ran to the passenger door. There was a lot of hugging going on inside, where there seemed to be no end of people, all with amazing colourful clothes on, women in droopy skirts with patches, men in long yellow boots.

One woman got out and embraced the driver. She was carrying a small soft pack, bedding most likely. She had very long dark hair, a long droopy dress with much decoration, a crushed velvet jacket and masses of hippie jewellery.

The bus drove away leaving her standing on the pavement. She waved and waved until the bus must have been long out of sight. Then Emma, the American woman, went out and greeted her. They embraced and laughed, Emma played some dud notes on her ocarina and the woman dropped her bag and danced. I went out to meet her.

'This is Thelma,' said Emma. 'She's just got off Henry's bus.'

'I saw,' I said. 'Hi.'

Thelma coughed in a chest-rattling, consumptive way. She had a Pre-Raphaelite beauty, dark, unhealthy and mysterious.

We drank tea together in Emma's room and listened to the Incredible String Band on the stereo Emma had bought from Rick for £11. Rick still had a lot of stereos to sell, all at knock-down prices. Thelma didn't want to buy one.

'Sounds like bad karma,' she said between coughs. She smoked roll-ups made of Dutch tobacco. 'I've just been to a festival,' she said.

'Where was it?' I asked.

'I don't know. There were lots of trees and beautiful people. You should have been there.'

'Henry's, like, this really amazing dude, right,' said Emma. 'He's really cool, he lives in a massive house in Wiltshire, he drives around all the festivals in his bus, he's just really turned on, man.'

'Yeah, I was tripping for days,' said Thelma. I noticed she had a lot of flowers woven into her hair, and she smelt very strongly of patchouli, tobacco and coffee, a heady mixture. We fell asleep on the bed, wrapped in each other's arms. There may have been some crude sexual fumblings on my part, but I was so heavily drugged I have no recollection of them. I felt guilty when I woke in the morning – or was it the afternoon? By now time had become a very blurred concept. Carol wouldn't even have got off the plane in America and I was in bed with someone else.

I let Cabbage out and crawled up the stairs to the only toilet in the house. I passed the only bathroom in the house and noticed something odd. The bath was full of thick red stuff. I shrugged and went to the toilet, which was as always in a disgraceful state. I cleaned it regularly, but it had finally beaten me. I went back to the bathroom and looked into the bath. I knew instantly it was full of jelly: the smell of strawberry flavour was very intense. I washed my hands in the filthy sink and sat on a small stool. A bath full of strawberry jelly! Something must have happened in the night. I floated back downstairs, passing Thelma on the landing where the poster for Lamb's Navy Rum still hung. 'I didn't put that there,' I said. She kissed me softly.

I carried on down the stairs, past the big mirror which now sat in the hall next to a box of records, a stereo and a small television set. I looked at myself. I was wearing a green silk shift thing, basically a woman's undergarment. It had little straps over the shoulder and hung to my knees. I was also wearing green wellington boots Rick had given me, an essential item for negotiating the floors of St Clements. I had thick rat's-taily hennaed hair tied in two bunches, a string of beads around my wrist and I looked half dead.

'Mad magic,' I said to my reflection.

Some time later that day, I sat in Emma's room with Thelma, listening to Van Morrison on the stereo.

I had never in my life been more relaxed or less worried. It was naturally connected to the drugs I had taken, but there was also something calm about Thelma. She was very graceful, very happy and yet I knew she had plenty of problems to deal with. Her chest being the main one. I had never heard someone with such a chronic cough, such wheezy breath. A miner on his last legs with emphysema would have sounded more healthy. She was painting a small picture.

'I dream a lot,' she said. 'So I paint my dreams.'

The painting was very grey, with what could have been street lamps or broken flowers dotted about. 'What was this one?'

'I was lost. For ages, lost, wandering,' she said with a cough.

'Yeah, I've had lost dreams,' I said, feeling wistful and lonely. 'And dreams about dogs.'

'Dogs?'

'Yeah, lying in long grass with loads of dogs, maybe I am a dog. Those are happy dreams. The dogs are really good friends; I know all of them. There's usually a tree, and sun, and sometimes I float above them.'

'Flying.'

'Yeah, sort of slow, floaty flying.'

'Sex dreams, Robert,' she said, kissed me and forced me gently down on the bed. Thelma and I never consummated our passion although she tried everything known to woman. I reverted to my pre-Carol flaccidity. I was a physical wreck, only I was not actually feeling ill because of the various colourful pills Rick gave me to try.

Thelma and I lay together in twisted silk debauchery, my hair a mass of red rat's tails, hers a thick throng of black twirls. I looked out of the window at the cloudless summer sky, listening to a mixture of British birds and Van Morrison, the ruins of my dome beginning to blend with the long grass in the back garden.

Some time that day Charlie emerged from a dank pit of sleep and found me in Emma's room. He looked dreadful, his hair hung like an old floorcloth, his clothes were ripped and dirty. He was carrying a carton of milk and had chocolate cake stains around his mouth.

'Wild times,' he said, making a roll-up with Thelma's tobacco.

'This is Thelma,' I said to Charlie. He nodded. 'This is Charlie. He's a genius.'

'We did a raid last night, man,' said Charlie.

Thelma looked slightly shocked at this. 'Oxford Poly, man. In through the skylight, down the rope we used at Magdalene, into the kitchens. We got so much cake, man, a huge sack of cake, and Rick got a ten-pound bag of jelly powder. Strawberry flavour.'

'I saw it,' I said.

'Did you try some?' asked Charlie. 'Gives you an amazing sugar high. Then we came back here, dumped the stuff and went off again. Rick's really going, man. I don't know what he's on. We did this house last night, yeah, up near Hilltop, went in through the front window. Rick was in the hall looking for wallets, I was in the kitchen looking for cake. They had loads of milk in their fridge but no cake so I took some bacon. Then the guy came down the stairs, he was there, man, we woke him up. Rick dived through the front window and legged it. I was stuck in the kitchen, so I hid behind the fridge, heard him call the police, he went upstairs again and I legged it with three pints of milk in a shopping bag. D'you want some?'

He offered Thelma the milk carton. She politely declined. I took a few huge swigs of cold milk and felt bloated and rather sick.

'I'm wrecked,' I said.

'Rick and I are off again tonight. D'you want to come?'

'Everything's fucked here. May as well.'

I sat at my workbench later that evening, sewing some leather belt pouches I was half way through making. Thelma sat on my bed and stroked Cabbage as we swapped our life stories. Thelma told me I was protected by a guardian angel. She said I had a blue aura. I felt very safe.

Rick fell into the room. 'Hi, maaaaaaan,' he said, laughing uncontrollably. He saw Thelma. 'Wow, a new chick!' he screamed. He fell on the floor by her feet. 'I'm Rick. Roberto's best friend.'

If Thelma had been slightly shocked at the revelation of Rick and Charlie's crime spree, she seemed utterly charmed by Rick himself.

'Hello, Rick. I'm Thelma,' she said.

'Thelma, far out name, maaaaaan.' He bounced up from the floor and threw himself at me. I went flying off my little chair and landed in the corner on some leather scraps. 'Hey, man, got any money?' he asked.

'Not a fucking penny,' I said. Rick had me pinned down by the shoulders.

'I still love you,' he said and gave me a kiss. Then he stood up and said to Thelma, 'Hey, I'm straight, Thelma, okay, maaaan. I just love Roberto, that's all, man. I love him in a manly way.'

'That's good,' said Thelma. She was transfixed by him, her mouth wide open, her eyes staring wildly as he bounced around the room.

'I need some money, man. I've got to go and visit a chick in Wales.'

'That's why I'm doing these pouches, man. If I finish them tonight I can sell them at Turl Trend in the morning. I'm getting £1.50 for each one. I've got to do ten, so I'll have £15.'

'What time can you sell them man?'

'I think the shop opens at nine.'

'Right, here's the plan,' said Rick, standing up. He pushed his hand into his pocket and pulled out some red and yellow pills. 'Take these, one every hour, go up to the Headington Hill service station, the one that's open all night.'

I nodded.

'Okay, there's a really cool student there called Russ, he's on night duty, all night, man. I can get some petrol from him. Okay, he'll let you in, you can drink Coke and eat chocolate there till you puke. I'll pick you up there at, shit, some time, I may not be able to stop long, you might have to jump in through an open window as I burn past, man.'

'Why can't you pick me up here?' I said, thinking of being uncomfortable in a garage waiting all night for Rick. The plan wasn't making a lot of sense, but then, not much did with Rick.

'Too risky, man, this place is being watched. I never leave through the front door, always over the back wall. Charlie knows all the routes, man. He's a fucking tracker dog.'

'Why can't you leave through the front door, Rick?' asked Thelma.

'I'm a wanted man, maaaan. I smashed a car up in Manchester, the pigs up there want to kill me, I'm on the run. There's loads of pigs want to get me but they're too slow.'

'Rick moves fast,' I said with admiration.

'The fastest mover, but not the fastest lover,' he said with a twirl. 'I like to make it last.' Thelma laughed. How did he do it? He looked like a crook, smoked like a crook, talked like a crook and women loved him. He was wearing a cheap, stolen black leather jacket, black gloves with rings on the outside like Alvin Stardust, terrible old stained jeans and black plimsoll shoes which would have made a tramp's eyes water, the smell was so bad. He had about five yellow teeth in his head, bad skin, chronic hair and bitten nails. Yet he was a pure ball of enthusiasm. I never saw him depressed.

'I'll be there,' I said.

At midnight I kissed Thelma good-bye in Emma's room. They were listening to Joni Mitchell and smoking dope. Hundreds of joss sticks were burning, Emma occasionally hitting a bum note on her ocarina, which contrasted badly with Joni's dulcet tones.

Cabbage's claws clicked quietly along the tarmac as I walked up the deserted footpath towards Headington. We passed under the cast-iron footbridge which Carol and I had walked across when I was living at Hilltop and I used to meet her from school. I missed her, but she had gone so far, she was so out of reach I couldn't understand the feeling, so I ignored it.

I had stuffed my big leather bag with smaller leather pouches. I had stitched only half of them and had a lot more to do. I remembered the pills Rick had given me and took one. By the time I got to the garage I was walking fast, my whole body itchy and bursting with movement.

'Hi, I'm Rob, mate of Rick's. He said I could wait for him here,' I said, much faster than I meant to. My nose felt like it was running and I kept wiping it and sniffing.

'Oh, sure, yeah, come in,' said Russ. He got up slowly and opened the door. He was tall, lean and good looking, a student of course, I could tell by his accent. He had a thick open book with him. The lighting was fluorescent and unforgiving, dazzlingly bright after my starlit walk. Cabbage tried to find somewhere to sleep.

'I'm Russell,' he said, shaking my hand. 'How is Rick?'

'He's fine. Yeah, he's out on a job tonight, man, he doesn't know what time he'll be back, but I've got to finish these leather pouches tonight so we can take them to Turl Trend in the morning, you know, the trendy shop on Turl Street, run by the bloke with the green hair, yeah, so if I can just sit somewhere and sew them up, 'cause I'm a leather worker you see, belts, pouches, wristbands, watch-straps and stuff, and then I can just sew them and it'll be cool and then Rick and I will go to Wales to see this chick he wants to see.'

The words poured forth in torrents, thousands of gal-lons of words, explanations and justifications. Russell sat in silence. I sat on a small pile of gallon oil cans and pulled out the leather pouches. I could just about sew them, but my fingers seemed to be all over the place. I then managed to find out about Russell without him saying a word. He just nodded or shook his head as I yabbered on.

'What d'you do then, Russell, like, what, you know, d'you study? 'Cause I saw your book, I wondered what you studied. I s'pose you're a stude, although you might not be, you might just like reading fat books, no, you're a stude, right, so what's the book, wow, philosophy, so which college, Brasenose? No, I used to be there, in the kitchens, man, I wasn't a stude, All Souls, no, Keeble, no, St John's, no, fine, no, Balliol, oh right, Balliol. Yeah, right, so philosophy, that must be great, all old Greek blokes with beards, oh right, not just that, what, other blokes, like Jean-Paul Sartre, not him, fair enough, who wrote your book? Schopenhauer, German bloke, bright, though, I bet, 'spect he wore small glasses like Jung and Freud, but they were more psychology, rather than philosophy, weren't they? I know a Jungian analyst called Mary, d'you know her? No, right, I wonder sometimes if I should have gone to university instead of worrying about politics and how fucked schools were, but I'd still be at school now, man, I'm seventeen and I'd be getting ready to do A levels. I'd never have stuck it.'

The roof of my mouth clegged together with my tongue. I had no saliva; it had dried out completely. Russell handed me a bottle of Coke, ready opened. I drank it all in one session and thankfully it calmed me down a bit.

'Took a pill that Rick gave me. I think it's some sort of speed,' I said a little more calmly.

'Yes, I imagine it must be,' said Russell with a smile.

The light slowly changed outside the little glass compartment, a few cars stopped by to get petrol, single men coming up to the window, paying Russell, sometimes buying a bar of chocolate. Russell didn't say much, he just listened to me wittering on as I sewed my leather pouches. By the time I had finished the last one, the sun was just showing above the suburban houses of Headington. A milk van clinked its way past. All was normality, the quiet before the storm.

Suddenly a gold BMW lurched into the forecourt at

speed, drove right around the glass compartment with the tyres screaming and smoke puffing off the rear wheel. It slowed to a halt outside the door and Rick jumped out. He was wearing an awful pair of sun-glasses like Graham Hill used to wear, with mirrored glass and steel bands at the sides with holes drilled in them. Charlie jumped out of the passenger side wearing a weird deerstalker hat. He bounced into the cubicle.

'Hi, Russ,' said Charlie, helping himself to chocolate. 'Robbie, this car is seriously fast, we just burnt off an MGB GT.'

'You're kidding.'

'Left him standing, man.'

Rick was putting some petrol in the car, and Russell started to look slightly ill at ease. Rick put in ten gallons and came to the payment window.

'Russ, man, I'll be back real soon and sort this out. You know I will,' he said with a gap-toothed smile. 'Come on, Roberto, let's sell some pouches and hit the road.'

'I'm staying,' said Charlie. 'I'm knackered.'

'Cool, Charlie. Thanks for your help, man,' said Rick, running round the car kicking the tyres. I opened the door, pulled the seat forward and Cabbage jumped in the back. I sat in the roomy front seat; it had wedgy bits at the side that held you in place. I pulled on the seat-belt and pushed myself into the seat. It was extremely comfortable. Rick climbed in the driver's seat, slammed the door and started the engine. So many lights came on in front of him it was dazzling – there were loads of dials, switches and controls, a radio set in the dashboard at a sexy angle and a row of cassette tapes set into a compartment in front of the gear stick.

We pulled out of the garage with such force that my

face hit the headrest as I tried to turn and wave at Russ and Charlie. We reached over 110 mph going down Headington Hill and I experienced the gut-wrenching sensation of high-performance brakes as we pulled to a halt at the traffic lights near St Clements.

We drove past Nirvana Hotel without a look. Rick was convinced it was being watched although I failed to see anyone sitting in an unmarked car. A few moments later we pulled up outside Turl Trend. There was no one about; it was 6.30 in the morning. Without saying a word, Rick drove off again, roared out of town and pulled to a halt in a small lay-by near Wolvercote. He put on a Status Quo tape very loud, pulled a lever and his seat went back. He fell asleep. Cabbage and I went for a walk along the tow path of the canal. The day was clear and bright, the air smelled sweet, I was a little dizzy from lack of sleep but I felt good.

When I got back to the car, Rick was still sleeping. I got in and turned off the music. Rick stirred but didn't wake. Cabbage got in the back seat, I put my seat back and immediately fell asleep too.

I woke up when the car started to move.

'I smell pigs, man,' said Rick as we accelerated out of the lay-by.

'What's the time, man?'

'It's gone eleven,' said Rick. 'You just let me sleep, Roberto. We could have been banged to rights there. I thought you were on guard.'

'Sorry,' I said. 'I just fell asleep.' We drove back into town and stopped outside the now busy Turl Trend shop. The man with the green hair was behind the counter serving some hippie women so that I had to wait. I looked out through the kaftans at Rick, sitting in a brand new gold BMW, looking absurd in his glasses.

A few moments later I got back into the car with fifteen crisp one pound notes in my back pocket. Rick started the car and we cruised slowly along the narrow lane, out into the High, and off.

Once past the Woodstock roundabout we rocketed along the A40, through Witney, where I'd been to school, where my father worked in a building society, where we couldn't stop in case someone saw me. Veering around the Burford roundabout at maximum speed, we shot across the Cotswolds. We cruised through Cheltenham, drove like crazy up the M5, touching 140 mph at times, cut west along the Ross Spur, rarely dropping below a hundred and then wound our way through Wales along back roads and smooth rolling A roads.

During this journey Rick explained that he and Charlie had stolen a car in Oxford, driven to Hungerford, broken into a chemist's and a supermarket to stock up on drugs and cake, then walked out of town and found a posh-looking house. Rick managed to burgle it through a rear kitchen window where he found a car key the like of which he'd never seen before. It didn't have notches, it was smooth with drilled indentations in it. He went from the kitchen into the garage and saw the car.

'I couldn't leave it, man,' said Rick. 'There was a Ford Escort next to it. That would have made loads more sense. I could have had that, I should have had that, but I couldn't leave this, man. I fucked up bad, man. I'm burning close to the end.'

Charlie had joined Rick in the house and found a deep-freeze, which was full of cheesecake and strawberries. Charlie filled the boot of the car with these, and some cake he had found in the kitchen, then drank all the milk in the fridge while Rick swore at him to hurry up. Then he and Rick opened the up-and-over garage door, pushed the car out and down the concrete drive and rolled it away as far as they could before starting it.

It sounded incredible but Rick had the key in the ignition. There was no hot wiring going on here; this was a serious car with serious electrics.

We stopped at a roadside café outside a small town in south-west Wales. I have no idea where, but Rick seemed to know where he was going.

By late evening we pulled into the front drive of a small brick-built bungalow with a wonderful view of the sea. The air was fresh and my hair whipped about in the stiff breeze. Rick knocked on the door, which was answered by a friendly looking middle-aged woman.

'Hi, Mrs Jones. I'm Rick, this is Rob. He's a rock singer. I was just seeing if Claire was in,' said Rick.

'Oh dear, you've just missed her,' the woman said with a lovely Welsh lilt. 'She's gone to London. Left this morning. There's a pity. Did you come far?'

'Only Oxford,' I said.

'Oh dear,' said the woman. 'Look, come in and have some tea. You need a rest: that's quite a drive. What a lovely car. Is it yours?' she asked me. I nodded and smiled as if to say, 'Afraid so. Bit pretentious, isn't it? But then I am a multi-million-pound rock star.'

We followed her into a large back room with a huge picture window. The sun was setting over the water; ships and yachts were picked out as silhouettes. There was a small garden right in front of the house planted with subtropical exotica: a beautiful prospect.

'Far out view, Mrs Jones,' said Rick.

'Yes, lovely, isn't it? Always changing,' she said from the kitchen. 'We never get bored of it.'

I sat down on a white leather sofa and almost im-

264

mediately fell asleep. It was so safe and quiet in the house, I wanted to stay.

Mrs Jones put on a Glenn Miller album and we drank tea listening to *Pennsylvania 6–5000*. Cabbage was given a saucer of milk which she lapped up rapidly.

'Yeah, well, Rob has to get back to London,' said Rick, during a lull in the music coming from the big mahogany hi-fi unit. 'He's doing a new album, so, you know, we'd better get going.'

'Fuck, shit, bollocks, cunts, arseholes, bastard, fuck, shit, shit, bollocks,' said Rick as we drove along slowly through the dark lanes.

'What's up?' I asked.

'Claire, her daughter, right, is pregnant. Claire Jones. I met her at, fuck, I don't remember, man, but I met her somewhere. I shagged her. It's my kid, right, maaan. She's gone to London to have an abortion. She said she would if I didn't show up in time. I forgot, man, I forgot which day I said I'd be here. I must have said yesterday. I'm so fucked up.'

'Maybe we can get to London in time,' I said, quite enjoying the prospect of a high-speed mercy dash.

'No, man, no way. We'd never make it. And we don't know where she is.'

'We could ask her mum.'

'No way, man. Her mum's really religious and that. She can't tell her mum anything. I can't blow it for her. She's beautiful, man. I came here to ask if she'd marry me.'

'Really?' I said.

'Yeah. I was going to settle down, get a job together, out here somewhere. Fisherman or something. Raise a kiddie, you know, live in a proper house. You know, I might have done the odd job now and again, down in Cardiff or something, just to furnish the house, but I'd cut right back on the drugs and shagging. She's great, Claire is. She's a brilliant chick, man, and she's gone to London for a fucking abortion. Shit.'

He pounded his fists on the steering wheel as we drove at a more gentle pace through long winding roads. It was impossible to say where we were: it was pitch black and both of us were tired to the point of hallucination. After about an hour we pulled into a lay-by. I got out, had a pee and breathed in the fresh night air. I couldn't see a thing. It was a cloudy night; there wasn't any light, nor a single star. Nothing.

'Really dark, man,' I said.

'Totally dark,' said Rick. 'We could be in outer space.'

I could hear Cabbage sniffing about in the leaves, a tinkling sound as she had a wee, then she hopped back into the car. We were all asleep within minutes. We slept like the dead.

I woke with a start when something seemed to hit the car. I opened my eyes and saw only brilliant light. I shifted about trying to get my bearings. Rick was asleep. The smell in the car was choking since we'd slept with the windows shut and the doors locked.

I stared outside. We were in a forest, next to a deserted road. A pine cone lay on the bonnet. I stared at the clock on the dash board: 5.38 a.m. Cabbage wagged her tail. She was huge with puppies, hungry, thirsty and needed to get out. I opened the door for her and Rick awoke with a scream. He thrashed about with his arms and I had to fall out of the car to avoid him hitting me.

'Fuck me, man, don't ever do that!' he screamed.

'What, what?' I shouted. 'I didn't do anything.'

'Don't wake me up like that, man. I need drugs to wake up. Shit man, I'm fucked up.' He opened the door and rolled out on to the ground. 'My back's seized up, man.

I'm locked up. Fuck, I've got no feeling in my legs. I think I've had a stroke.' He pulled himself through the leaves like a wounded rabbit. 'Put a bullet through my head, man. Don't leave me to suffer,' he said through gritted teeth. 'If you love me, man, you'll do it.'

'I haven't got a gun.'

'Use a rock, cave my head in, man. The police'll understand when they do the autopsy, they'll see that I was crippled with pain and you'll get off, man. Do it. Do it!' he screamed.

I stared about in a panic. I couldn't drive, we were miles from anywhere in a stolen car with no food, very little money and a pregnant dog. Rick was writhing about in agony now. Cabbage thought it was a game and started to worry at his sleeve. Suddenly Rick started laughing and stood up, opened his fly and urinated against a tree.

'Oh, fucking hell, man! I was really worried,' I said.

'You'd never have killed me, would you, Roberto? I knew I could trust your humanity, man. Come on, let's get some fucking breakfast.'

We got in the car and drove like fools along the endless forest road. It was very beautiful, but as every bend was taken at a speed which made the tyres scream out, it wasn't very relaxing. We eventually hit open farm land, passing milk lorries and tractors, roared into a small town and found a café. We ordered the biggest breakfast they could do. I got two cans of Chappie dog food from a corner shop, the café owner opened them and Cabbage ate the lot.

By the time we were back in the car we had £4 left.

'How much petrol?' I asked.

'Half a tank. This thing drinks the stuff,' shouted Rick. We were doing about 95 mph at the time. We eventually hit the M4 somewhere outside Swansea, and Rick really put his foot down. At one point we raced with a man on a motor bike, both of us doing around 120 mph. It was terrifyingly dangerous: one false move and we could have killed the motor cyclist, another car's occupants, ourselves, even people living in houses near the motorway.

After the Severn Bridge, Rick took the M5, heading north. We pulled off the motorway at a junction and skidded to a halt. Rick got out, ran behind a wooden fence and had a very public bowel movement.

'Just made it,' he said as he got back in the car. 'I was touching cloth.'

There was a hippie couple hitching at the slip road to the motorway. Rick pulled up right by them and opened the electric window.

'Where you going, man?' he asked.

'Worcester,' they said happily.

'Get in, we're in a hurry.'

They climbed in the back and Rick was moving off before they'd shut the door.

'Hi, I'm Phil, this is Fiona.'

'I'm Rick,' said Rick. 'This is my mechanic Rob. We're professional bike riders, you know, Isle of Man TT. Stuff like that.'

'Right,' said Phil, looking rather alarmed as our speed climbed well over one hundred mph.

'Yeah, man, we've just come back from France, had the bike rebuilt by Rob's firm in Cardiff.'

'Yeah, my firm,' I said. Seventeen years old, thin as a rake, not shaving, long red hair and a pregnant dog. They didn't look like they bought it.

'Is this your car?' asked the rather astute Fiona.

'Yeah man, this is my BMW. We won the Isle of Man TT last year, then a few races in the States, man. Daytona,

Ohio, New York, all over, man. Just bought this for cash. She's a beauty, huh?'

A red light started to flash beneath the speedometer, accompanied by a sharp, science-fiction-style repeating buzzing noise. The car started to shake a little, and I noticed Fiona grab Phil's hand in the back. Moments later we appeared to take off. The bang was so loud I think we all screamed; it seemed to lift the back end of the car off the road. I looked at Rick; his face was white with horror. The car lurched wildly, the G forces throwing the two hitchhikers and Cabbage across the roomy rear seats. The car vibrated so much I lost clear vision; everything seemed to be coming apart.

'Shit, blow-out, man,' said Rick, gripping the wheel and fighting to control the lurches. The alarm was still sounding, warning lights were flashing all over the place.

'Fully auto,' said Rick. 'Solid state electronics, warns of oncoming hazards.' He dabbed the brakes and the car slowly regained its stability. 'I had it specially fitted.'

We somehow managed to slow from 120 to stationary with one tyre a mass of ripped, tangled steel belting and charred rubber. For all his bravado, his drug abuse, his sexual profligacy and his ludicrous lies, Rick could drive a car extraordinarily well. He pushed this car to the very limit of its capabilities, but never further. He may have gone around roundabouts too fast for sensible people who want to continue living, but never once did the tyres lose their grip, he may have braked hard when he came up behind a car doing a mere seventy on the motorway, but never once did he skid.

Rick jumped out and opened the boot, and we both worked maniacally, unbolting the smouldering tyre, jacking the car up and replacing it with the spare. All the time we were looking up the long stretch of busy motorway for a police car. They were bound to stop if they saw us. The two hitchhikers sat in the back of the car in abject terror. They didn't move a muscle.

'We've done it, man,' said Rick as he threw the jack and spanner into the boot. 'We've had a blow-out and changed the fucker before the pigs saw us. Good omen, man.'

'I know what,' I said, nodding at the hitchhikers. 'Let's pretend we're aliens.'

'Far out,' said Rick.

'Yub dullu blug,' I said.

'Mollo cholla bolla,' said Rick as he got back into the car.

I pointed at the dashboard as Rick started the engine. 'Yub dullu blug,' I said. Rick turned to the people in the back.

'Do not fear,' he said. 'We mean you no harm. We have to get back to the mother ship.'

He roared off into the fast lane and accelerated up to the statutory 140 mph before turning and saying to them, 'The dog carries the seed of our people. We must protect her.'

We travelled as far as Cheltenham in silence. I was doing lots of alien-looking-out-of-the-window acting. Rick pulled off at the slip road and we let the hitchhikers out.

'Good luck on your journey,' said Phil.

We stifled our laughter until we had screeched off the roundabout and swung on to the A road into Cheltenham.

'I need to steal some food,' said Rick as we sat in heavy traffic in the middle of town. He pulled off on a side road and roared past a police car coming in the other direction.

'Shit, man, they clocked us,' said Rick. I turned and

watched, and though they didn't turn around to follow us, my heart raced as Rick lurched the car around the backstreets.

'There must be a food shop we can rip off somewhere round here,' he said. 'We need one with a good getaway: just run in, take what you want and leg it.'

'But what if those cops saw us?' I said. 'They might be radioing base and all that.'

'Fuck that paranoia, man. We're past that shit, we're on another plane of reality, man.'

Rick swung the car down a narrow one-way street, suddenly pulling to a halt with a heart-stopping jolt. A large uniformed policeman was standing right in our path with his hand held up.

This was it. It was over. Reality poured in through the windows as fast as water in a submerged car. This was it. I was going to prison. The policeman walked slowly up to Rick's window. Rick pressed the button and the window slid open.

'Is this your vehicle, sir?' the policeman asked.

'No, officer. It's my dad's,' said Rick.

'I see. Would you mind stepping out of the car, sir?'

Rick got out without so much as a glance at me. He was holding the ignition key as he talked, tapping it in the palm of his hand. People walked past the car and stared in at me. This was the town my parents came from. This was where I visited my grandmother, this was where I had been a good, short-haired boy in shorts who helped with the washing up. I had been for picnics on the surrounding hills and heard stories about what my mum and dad did when they were kids.

There was a tap on the window by my side. I nearly jumped out of my skin. A man in an ugly light brown suit was squatting down smiling at me. He motioned for me to open the window. It took me a moment to find the button.

'Good morning, sir. How are you?' he asked politely.

'Fine, thanks,' I said. My pulse seemed to shake my body with each beat.

'That your dog, sir?'

'Yes. She's about to have pups,' I said.

'Is she now? And where are you from then?'

I told him my name, my address, my date of birth. Everything. I just wanted to get it over. Soon I would get out of the car and he'd put the handcuffs on me. Cabbage would be taken to a dog pound and put to sleep. I would go to prison and have all my hair cut off. This was it.

The policeman wrote it all down methodically, very calmly and politely. He didn't ask me whose car it was, why I was in it, who the driver was, nothing like that.

Rick sat in the car beside me and started up the engine. Even then it didn't dawn on me. I assumed they had asked him to drive it to the police station where we would be formally arrested.

'Okay, man. Now we move fast,' said Rick. We pulled away from the kerb and merged with the traffic. I glanced back at the conferring police officers standing on the pavement.

'What happened? What are they going to do?' I asked, my voice high-pitched and panicked.

'They bought it, man. They couldn't do nothing. Checked up at the station, no car like this reported stolen in this area. See, this is Cheltenham and Gloucester. The car comes from the Thames Valley area. I had the key; no way could you hot wire this baby. I told them it was my dad's car and I was insured to drive it, but he didn't want me to drive it this far so I was really worried he'd find out. He asked me what was in the boot, I told him. He asked me what the registration number was, I told him. They let us go, man. You are being driven by a professional, man. I told you, good omen, man. They'll never fucking stop us now.'

'I told them my name and address,' I said quietly once we had left the town.

'What!' said Rick. The acceleration died, and we started to cruise along.

'I thought we were being arrested. I told them my name and address.'

'Your real name and address?' he asked coldly.

'Yeah.'

'Why?' he screamed.

'I thought this was it. We'd been stopped by a cop, you'd got out, this other bloke asked me questions. I just wanted to get it over with.'

'I don't believe it,' shouted Rick.

'Well, how was I meant to know?' I said, on the verge of tears.

'You fucking stupid wanker, you fuck-headed cunt-faced stupid-arseholed toss bag. Fuck fuck fuck.' He smashed his fists against the steering wheel. 'We've got to dump the car.'

'Why?' I said.

'Because they're gonna come and get you, man. We've got to dump the car and head for the coast, flee the fucking country, man.'

'Oh fuck it, Rick. I can't be bothered,' I said, my head in my hands.

'What d'you mean? You want to go to Borstal? Get beaten up and buggered by some thick skinhead every ten minutes? You wouldn't stand a fucking chance, man. A wimp like you, they'd eat you for breakfast.'

'I don't care.'

Rick drove the last forty miles at a very sensible ninety-five, pulling up in a lay-by on the A40 just outside Witney. We locked the car, wiped everything with my T-shirt to remove our fingerprints, though it seemed pointless to me as they would get me anyway, then we walked into the town. It was early evening. People walked along Witney's small, tree-lined streets looking innocent. Innocence is a valuable commodity, a wonderful thing and a hard one to appreciate, unless you've been guilty. We went to the Royal Oak pub, a favourite hang-out for Witney's small population of long-hairs. I drank an orange juice while Rick hassled people for beer and cigarettes. I felt hollow and didn't care what happened. There were people in the pub I had gone to school with, who were still studying for their A levels. They tried to speak to me but I couldn't be bothered to talk back. I just stroked Cabbage's head under the table and stared into the distance.

'Where d'you want to go, Roberto?' asked Rick in the Royal Oak's rear car park. I stared at the starlit sky.

'St Clements,' I said. Rick embraced me, looked at me and smiled. He said nothing. I climbed in the back of a Vauxhall Viva van for some reason. Rick was holding the door open for me. We drove into Oxford with a bearded and talkative man at the wheel. Rick sat in the passenger seat, chain smoking and talking back. The van dropped me off outside Nirvana Hotel.

Cabbage and I went inside. A woman called Dymphna had moved into my room. I didn't care. The house was a wreck. I didn't care about that either. Thelma had moved out and left me a nice note with her new address. I did mind about that but I had no energy to make a fuss.

Emma walked past me and said, 'You look terrible.'

I asked Dymphna if I could sleep in her bed. She said she didn't mind. I dropped three blue pills that Rick had given me and collapsed.

14

Newbury Blues

I awoke to the sound of loud knocking on the front door. I knew what it was. I turned around and saw a woman I didn't know cuddled up behind me. I was in my room, but it was different. Cabbage was nowhere to be seen. I pulled on some green flared trousers I found on the floor. They weren't mine, but they fitted. Near them was a scoop-necked, flared-sleeved, tie-dyed shirt. I pulled that over my head and slipped my feet into my fetid yellow and red boots.

I answered the door to two policemen. They asked me for my name, I told them, they read me my rights and arrested me.

'Are you going to come quietly, son, or are we going to have to use the cuffs?'

'I'll come very quietly,' I said. The officer escorted me to the small Ford Escort police car and I got in the back. They started to drive south out of Oxford; we arrived at Newbury police station an hour later. A very large, short-haired officer in a spotless white shirt held the door open for me.

'Straight inside, son. Any funny business and you will be banged to rights, you hear me. I'm not mincing words.'

'Okay, yes, I understand,' I said, walking into the newly built station. I was shown into a small office where two plain clothes policemen stood waiting. They offered me a chair, and much to my surprise actually went through the good cop, bad cop routine. Even by the age of seventeen I had witnessed this so many times on *Dixon of Dock Green*,

Z Cars and *Softly, Softly* that it had become a cliché. Yet here I was, sitting opposite a sympathetic young policeman who was writing down what I said and being shouted at in the face by an older, more brutal-looking policeman with close-cropped hair.

I experienced an hour of questioning about who I was, where I lived, who I knew, how I ended up in a stolen car in the middle of Cheltenham, where the car was left, who the driver was.

'There's no point trying to protect him, sunshine. We'll get him soon enough,' said the brutal one.

'His name's Rick,' I said.

'Rick what?' shouted the brute.

'I don't know. He only ever told me it was Rick.'

'Where did you meet him?' said gentle.

'He came to my house.'

'Your house?' shouted brute.

'Yeah, in St Clements. Where I was arrested.'

'That's not your house, is it? That's a squat. That's a stolen house, Robert. You're a thief, aren't you?' said the brute triumphantly.

'No, we have a legitimate right to live there. We have claimed squatters' rights. It's from a law dating back to the time of the Crusades, when the knights who went off to fight in the Holy Land didn't come back, you could live in their castles.'

'It's a squat. You're a squatter, a vagrant and a thief,' said the brutal officer without much interest in my knowledge of medieval law.

'Did he say where he got the car from?' asked the nice one.

'No,' I lied. 'But I sort of worked out by the end that he probably shouldn't have it.'

'Probably shouldn't have it,' the brute copied my

277

delivery. 'You're in a brand new BMW motor car with a kid who barely shaves and you surmise that maybe he probably shouldn't have it.'

'He could have been a pop star,' I said.

'Listen, Robert,' said the brutal one. 'You came to Newbury with this Rick character on a two-man crime spree. I saw you with my own eyes,' he lied. Strange as it may seem, this did come as a shock to me. 'You were in the car park in the middle of town, you broke into the chemist's, stole drugs, did a lot of damage and then went off and stole the BMW. I saw you here, Robert. I know you did it.'

'No,' I said, 'I spent all night in a garage with a bloke called Russell, on Headington Hill. He's a student, a philosophy student at Balliol.'

'Why did you spend the night in a garage?' asked the nice one.

'Well, I couldn't sleep, and I knew Russell would be there. You see, I make leather stuff, bags and belts and pouches. I was finishing some leather pouches for a shop I sell stuff to in Turl Street. I'm not a thief, I'm a leather worker.'

'Yeah, and I'm Sherlock Holmes,' said the brutal one.

They threw me in a cell and slammed the door. Well, they didn't throw me, they ushered me rather politely. Ten years before Greenham Common, Newbury police station didn't see a lot of action.

I was hauled out of the cell about an hour later. They took my fingerprints and those two photographs with the number under your chin. Two hours after that a sturdy-looking probation officer wearing a nice, light suit was shown into my cell. He sat down opposite me and asked me what had happened. I told him. He explained what would happen to me as regards standard police procedure and looked a little shocked when he discovered I hadn't been charged with anything.

'They're not supposed to take your mug shots or finger-prints before they've charged you,' he said. 'I'll have a chat with the station sergeant about that. Have you had your phone call?'

'What's that?' I asked.

Without saying anything, he got up and left the cell. A few moments later I was taken from my cell by another police officer and shown down a corridor to a pay phone. I made a reverse charge call to my parents' house. My sister answered.

'It's Rob. Is Mum or Dad there?'

'No, they're playing tennis,' said my sister. So normal.

'Oh, right, well, I'm in Newbury police station. I've been arrested for stealing a car. I haven't done it, but they think I have. I need to be bailed out.'

There was a silence. 'Hello.'

'Why are you there?' asked my sister. Clearly the informa-tion hadn't registered.

'I'm being held in the police station, I'm under arrest. I've been busted. Get Mum or Dad to come and bail me out.'

'All right.'

'And Cabbage is about to have puppies.'

'All right.'

'Newbury police station.'

'Where's that?'

'I don't know. Newbury.'

'All right.'

I put the phone down. That was it. There was nothing to do. I was locked in my cell. The following morning I was taken to the adjoining magistrates' court. There was no one there except a cleaner, a police officer – the nice one who interviewed me – a magistrate and an old man who drew my portrait rather well and very fast. I was classified as a vagrant, which I objected to politely, explaining that I had lived and worked at the one address for at least a month, and that I was a legitimate resident under the squatting laws of 1150 or thereabouts.

'A vagrant,' said the magistrate, a bored old man. I was held for another twenty-four hours pending investigations, twenty-three of which I spent in the cell with one book: a boy's adventure story which took me an hour to read and whose ending I had guessed by page thirty. I lay looking at the ceiling, feeling strangely relaxed. My only worry was Cabbage. I worried no one would look after her, that she would have her puppies soon. Other than that, I was very happy to let events take their course. At least I wasn't on the run. I was sick of cars and stealing and keeping an eye out for the police. I was sick of little pills of different colours and sleeping badly and riding on fast motor bikes.

I ran through what I could remember of my journey to that cell. I realized that it was all so banal. Stealing a car was so banal. All crime is banal, boring, pointless. Maybe if you're starving, or your children are starving, you can justify a crime to yourself, but I never needed anything we stole – it was only ever a burden when we had it. I had learned a lesson before I was arrested, that getting hold of something by stealing it removes its value. Stealing things was, therefore, pointless.

I looked at the scratchings on the cell wall. 'I'll do me bird man. Nobby 1971,' 'Dave woz 'ere in '73' 'There's no justice. Off the pigs. Spart '72.' A strange male attitude, butching it out, being strong and taking your punishment: an absurd idea and one I wanted no part of. I didn't want to take my punishment, I wanted to cry. I did cry, a hopeless, stupid, pitiful cry of pointlessness. I didn't cry for long. I remembered the phrase I had seen in Llanbedr. To live outside the law, you must be honest. I had lived outside the law and taken people who lived inside it as fools. They may have been fools but they were powerful fools and I'd pushed my luck. I had ignored the law and the law had won.

I didn't want to leave a mark in that cell wall. 'Rob was 'ere, Sept '73, man.' I wasn't proud to be there but I wasn't ashamed either. I wasn't really there for stealing, we did nothing with the stuff we'd stolen, we always gave it back. We'd borrowed it without asking. That's not to justify it, but that's how I saw it. I'd done it for the rush, the thrill. In Rick I had met someone with a vital spark of immoral energy the like of which I had never seen before. There was something so liberating in that total disregard for law, order, morality, decency and empathy which Rick embodied. It's a mood which clearly a lot of young men feel at some time, a dangerous feeling for the rest of us, one which is normally channelled into sport or heavy drinking, fighting on the street or war.

I was brought up in a well-disciplined, decent, law-abiding environment. I was told very clearly how bad it was to steal, how important it was to care for other people. I believed that, I believed it even as I was swinging around the country in a stolen gold-coloured BMW.

Rick somehow took the banal dream that men have of owning such a car and laughed at it. That was what was so attractive to me about being with him in it. It meant nothing, this amazing piece of technology which could move you so fast, it meant nothing.

'I've realized that possessions mean nothing,' I said to the stocky probation officer when he came to see me again. 'I feel so much happier. It's like what Krisnamurti says about beliefs and faith. It's just baggage we don't need, it weighs us down.'

The probation officer looked at me as if I were slightly mad, with a frozen smile and a slight nod. I had been in the cell alone for twenty-three hours a day for three days. He sighed and said, 'Okay, Robert, you're going to a committal proceeding today. Now, if you don't get bailed out this morning, you'll be held in the young offenders' wing at Winchester Prison until your case comes up. That could be as long as three months. Have you called your family?'

'Yeah, days ago.'

'And they haven't been in touch?'

'Not as far as I know.'

'Okay, I'll go and see what's going on. I don't think you should go to Winchester. It's not a very good place to be. All you'll learn there is how to steal more cars and break into more houses.'

He got up and left. After a few minutes the brutal police officer opened the door. 'All right, son, out you come. Any funny business and I'll spread you over the floor like raspberry jam, and I'm not mincing words. Savvy?'

'Yes,' I said and walked past him into the back of a police van. The prospect of three months in Winchester Prison Young Offenders' Wing did not fill me with glee, but there was still something relaxing about having no responsibility for your life, just doing as you were told, having no decisions to make. I looked out of the rear window of the noisy police Transit van. To my surprise I saw my mum and dad following us in the family car. They were looking stern faced and shocked in the grey morning light. It later transpired that when my sister had told my mother of my phone call from Newbury police station, my mother was so furious she refused to bail me out and refused to tell my father. 'Serves him right!' she shouted. It was over breakfast several days later that my sister finally spilt the news to my father, who then rushed to the rescue. Now, on the short drive to Hungerford, they were watching their little lad in the back of a police van with filthy long hair and wearing stupid clothes. No one in the family had been in any trouble with the law as far back as anyone could remember, on either side of the family.

The court case was short. They bailed me out for £150 surety on fifteen charges of taking and driving, breaking and entering, and petty theft. As I was classified as a vagrant, I was bailed to live at home with my parents.

The drive home was long and slightly unpleasant, although neither of my parents did a rant. My father was very shocked and shaken. A report of my crimes would appear in the local paper, he would have to face the bank managers and solicitors of Witney now they knew his son was a drug-crazed car thief. As I sat in the back seat, alone and relaxed, I started to tell them what had happened. A strange feeling came over me, one I never remember experiencing before. I didn't have to embroider, I didn't have to elaborate one bit. I told my mum and dad what had actually happened, for the first time in my life. The story was big enough and outrageous enough to stand up by itself. It was almost as if I had lived outside the law, which made me honest. As the true story unfurled, one hundred per cent accurate with no embellishment, I sailed. I had a life at last. A history, a solid lump of past I could stand on. I was someone, someone with a series of problems and difficulties, I was filling up, becoming colourful and interesting.

And only once during my hour-long explanation did

my mother, clearly furious with me, say, 'What did I say to you, my lad?'

Mum and Dad took me to St Clements to pick up Cabbage. It was strange walking back into Nirvana Hotel, almost as if I'd never lived there. Charlie opened the door and I quickly informed him he was okay, they didn't know anything about him. There was no sign of Rick. Charlie didn't know where he was.

Cabbage was so big she could barely walk. Charlie had looked after her well but she was thrilled to see me. I picked up some tools, some leather and what meagre possessions I had managed to keep track of and filled the tidy boot of my father's car with my decaying, tattered life.

The Ford's tyres crunched on the gravel of my parents' drive and, almost a year to the day since my push bike had done the same as I'd left home, I arrived back. Thinner, dirtier, infected with head lice and a lot older. I had a lot of baths and all my clothes were boiled. I had to apply copious amounts of Prioderm liquid to my head and wrap my hair in a towel as the millions of head lice wriggled in their itchy death throes. I then had to comb through the great mop of tangled locks with an ultra-fine-tooth comb to remove the lice eggs. Millions of them formed a grey paste on the teeth of the comb.

Cabbage had seven puppies one morning, all of which survived. She lived happily with them in an old coal bunker in the back garden which I cleaned out and lined with newspaper and blankets. Every morning I opened the shutter and seven puppies would yap and tumble their way out.

I received long letters from Carol in Alamogordo, New Mexico. She had been taken ill on the plane on the way to America, was rushed to hospital in Boston and had an ovarian cyst removed. She recovered very quickly and flew to see her mother. She sent me pictures of herself walking in the desert. I wrote long and probably quite weird letters to her.

About a month into my stay a police car pulled up in the drive of my parents' house and I was re-arrested, taken to Witney police station and re-charged with one offence: allowing myself to be driven in a vehicle knowing it to be taken without the consent of the owner.

It sounded reasonable. While I was in the police station I was told that Rick had verified my story and taken all the blame himself. I remember feeling very sad, hearing somehow in this that he had been broken, had lost his spirit, stopped fighting. I was very grateful. I still think it was an incredibly honourable thing to do, but I also felt worried that he might think I had grassed him up. The police officer wouldn't tell me how or where he was caught.

I had to visit a probation officer in Witney who listened to my stories with a delightful attentiveness. He wrote me a glowing, adoring Social Enquiry Report, which I wish I had been able to keep for my own emotional sustenance. I have never before or since received such a litany of unadulterated praise. All my ideas came across as angelic, I was the Mother Theresa of hippies, a Gandhi of the alternative society, an Isambard Kingdom Brunel of dome building.

My court case was a brief affair, held in a small magistrates' court in Hungerford. It was the first time I had seen Rick since I'd climbed out of the Vauxhall Viva van with half my brain missing. He looked happy enough, talking away to two prison officers who escorted him. I was wearing a clean shirt and tie, my clean hair tied neatly in a pony-tail, and I had a good lawyer at my side. Rick was on his own.

My charge was read out; I pleaded guilty. The three magistrates, uniformly middle-aged middle-class men, conferred briefly and gave me two years' conditional discharge. They explained this meant that if I were caught for no matter how small a crime, this charge would be taken into consideration alongside it.

Rick stood up next. They read out his charges. It took about six minutes. Car thefts, unpaid parking tickets, shoplifting offences, breaking and entering, stealing petrol, stealing drugs from chemists' shops, house burglaries, school break-ins, more car thefts, more unpaid parking tickets, and dozens of driving offences like crossing red lights and not stopping when asked to do so by a police officer. It was a litany of road madness stretching from Manchester to Plymouth.

A police officer explained that Rick was arrested while sleeping in a stolen tent in west Wales, I guessed near his girlfriend Claire's house. He didn't put up any resistance and had been very helpful to the police in their enquiries.

He was held on remand until he went to crown court. His charges were too serious to be dealt with by magistrates. He gave me a quick smile as he was walked away by the prison guards.

I was free to go. The relief was palpable. Although I had been assured by the lawyer that I wouldn't go to Borstal, it was always a nagging worry. My mother and father were clearly relieved, and the mood was decidedly more cheerful on the journey home.

I stayed with my parents a while longer. They were incredibly forgiving and accommodating and during my time there I made enough leather stuff actually to save some money. It was during this period I started experimenting with basic footwear design. I didn't want to make decorative hippie trinkets any more. I had dreams of setting up a rurally based collective shoe factory. I built an experimental shoe, a one-size-fits-all leather flipper I named a Goof Boot. One wet night I walked from my parents' house to a friend who lived up the road, all of half a mile. By the time I got there my prototype Goof Boots had completely disintegrated, utterly fallen apart. I entered my friend's house with some inexplicable scraps of leather tied to my sodden bare feet. But it was a start, and I knew Goof Boots were really going to catch on.

Postscript

Since my brief flirtation with the world of crime, I have grown to believe firmly in the Buddhist concept of karma. In the last twenty-two years I have been burgled four times, and each burglary left my lowly flat decimated: the door kicked to matchwood, everything I owned soiled, broken and smashed. In each case the thieves got away with under £5 in loose change which I kept in an ornate pot. During the last burglary they smashed the pot, presumably because it was empty. I have never had a car stolen but I have lost seven car radios and every car I've owned has been broken into and gutted. I can recall twelve separate occasions of finding my car with speakers ripped from doors, alarm systems gleefully wrenched from under the bonnet, windows smashed. So, on reflection, I calculate my karma is about even. Any further losses on my part guarantee my place in Nirvana.

Most of these petty offences were carried out by white males under the age of eighteen. I asked a dubious car stereo fitter with a murky garage around the back of King's Cross what a car radio was worth. 'If it was a good one and it worked,' he said, 'maybe a pound.' He opened a door at the back of his premises. Inside was piled over 500 car radios. 'The market's flooded,' he explained. 'I don't want them, car boot sales is the only place you can shift them.' These young men don't do it for the money; they do it because it's a gas.

My solution to solving crime on a personal level? Don't

own anything, and if you do, own only rubbish and don't value it. You'll be much happier.

Where are They Now?

Allie lives in Western Australia with her husband and six children.

Gary, Helen, and most of the urban peasants still live in Oxford.

Daisy, their daughter, is a policewoman.

Llanbedr is now a rather swish private house with a lovely garden.

Napoleon is amazingly similar and lives somewhere in the West Country.

Duncan went on to become a quite successful television producer at the BBC.

Terry was knocked off his push bike and killed by a teenage joy rider.

The student with the beard and the Che Guevara poster is now a Labour MP.

Charlie is a computer programmer and juggler, and lives in Bath, occasionally in the company of his five children.

Carol lives in Oxford with her two children and runs a popular bar.

Rosie became Ma Prem Cutira when her guru renamed her. It means 'little hut of love'.

David lives in Oxford, still in the same house, still making leather items.

Cabbage spent her declining years on a farm in south-west Cork, Ireland.

The Professor of Law teaches at Michigan University.

Mike is now a successful jewellery designer.

Rick, after serving a custodial sentence, had a brief flirtation with punk stardom and is now happily married and working as a train driver for British Rail.

Pirate Paul lives in Bath and recycles building materials.

John Paul Rous murdered a volunteer care worker at an Oxford hostel for the mentally ill in 1993, and is now being held in Broadmoor.

Thelma studied painting at the Royal Academy and is a successful portrait painter.

READ MORE IN PENGUIN

In every corner of the world, on every subject under the sun, Penguin represents quality and variety – the very best in publishing today.

For complete information about books available from Penguin – including Puffins, Penguin Classics and Arkana – and how to order them, write to us at the appropriate address below. Please note that for copyright reasons the selection of books varies from country to country.

In the United Kingdom: Please write to *Dept. EP, Penguin Books Ltd, Bath Road, Harmondsworth, West Drayton, Middlesex UB7 ODA*

In the United States: Please write to *Consumer Sales, Penguin USA, P.O. Box 999, Dept. 17109, Bergenfield, New Jersey 07621-0120.* VISA and MasterCard holders call 1-800-253-6476 to order Penguin titles

In Canada: Please write to *Penguin Books Canada Ltd, 10 Alcorn Avenue, Suite 300, Toronto, Ontario M4V 3B2*

In Australia: Please write to *Penguin Books Australia Ltd, P.O. Box 257, Ringwood, Victoria 3134*

In New Zealand: Please write to *Penguin Books (NZ) Ltd, Private Bag 102902, North Shore Mail Centre, Auckland 10*

In India: Please write to *Penguin Books India Pvt Ltd, 706 Eros Apartments, 56 Nehru Place, New Delhi 110 019*

In the Netherlands: Please write to *Penguin Books Netherlands bv, Postbus 3507, NL-1001 AH Amsterdam*

In Germany: Please write to *Penguin Books Deutschland GmbH, Metzlerstrasse 26, 60594 Frankfurt am Main*

In Spain: Please write to *Penguin Books S. A., Bravo Murillo 19, 1° B, 28015 Madrid*

In Italy: Please write to *Penguin Italia s.r.l., Via Felice Casati 20, I-20124 Milano*

In France: Please write to *Penguin France S. A., 17 rue Lejeune, F-31000 Toulouse*

In Japan: Please write to *Penguin Books Japan, Ishikiribashi Building, 2-5-4, Suido, Bunkyo-ku, Tokyo 112*

In Greece: Please write to *Penguin Hellas Ltd, Dimocritou 3, GR-106 71 Athens*

In South Africa: Please write to *Longman Penguin Southern Africa (Pty) Ltd, Private Bag X08, Bertsham 2013*